Technology
for Motor Mechanics

PART 1 – Tools and Materials

# Technology
# for Motor Mechanics

## PART 1 (FIRST YEAR) Tools and Materials

### SECOND EDITION

**S. C. Mudd**, F.I.M.I., A.M.B.I.M., M.A.E.T.

Deputy Head, Department of Technician
and Motor Vehicle Engineering,
Huddersfield Technical College

Edward Arnold

© S. C. MUDD 1972

*First published 1967*
by Edward Arnold (Publishers) Ltd
41 Bedford Square
London WC1B 3DQ

*Reprinted 1970*
**Second edition 1972**
*Reprinted 1973, 1975, 1977, 1978*

ISBN: 0 7131 3270 1

Printed Offset Litho in Great Britain by
Cox & Wyman Ltd
London, Fakenham and Reading

# Preface to the Second Edition

In all the various occupations involved in the sale, service, and repair of motor vehicles each individual worker is expected to have a fair knowledge of subjects or skills other than those directly concerned with his day-to-day tasks. This requirement is reflected in the revised syllabuses of the City and Guilds of London Institute, the Part One Examination now being common to all the *Motor Vehicle Craft* subjects.

This book has been revised with the intention of complementing the *Technology* syllabus material and assisting with the *Associated Studies* at the Part One level. It should be of great assistance to students following the various schemes of Integrated Training now operated by colleges and employers.

Although SI units are used generally in the book the requirements of the motor industry, and of the teaching syllabuses, have made necessary the continued use of British, American and Unified threads. Details of these threads and their corresponding spanner sizes are therefore retained.

It is hoped that both teachers and instructors will find the book acceptable for use as a classbook, so eliminating the time-wasting practice of giving and taking notes. In this way it is possible to devote more time to the real work of teaching and learning.

Huddersfield                                                      S. C. MUDD
1972

# Acknowledgements

The author wishes to tender his sincere thanks to those of his colleagues whose criticisms, assistance, and encouragement have helped to make this book possible.

The author is also indebted to the following companies who provided a great deal of the source material and generously granted permission for its use. Many thanks to:

C. and J. Hampton Ltd.

Gordon Tools Ltd.

Firth Brown Tools Ltd.

Moore and Wright (Sheffield) Ltd.

J. W. Pickavant and Co. Ltd.

'Epco' Ltd.

The British Motor Corporation.

The Rootes Group of Companies.

Extract from BS 1710:1960 is reproduced by permission of the British Standards Institution.

# Contents

# Workshop Safety

In any society rules and regulations must be devised for the guidance and benefit of all concerned; the garage is no exception. These rules are necessary to make the garage a safe, efficient and healthy place in which to work. A clean and well-ordered shop is also much more attractive to customers.

**Tidiness.** The most important rule of all is tidiness. A good mechanic detests untidiness and the accumulation of dirt that always goes with it. Vehicle repairing is never clean work but a good mechanic does not have to be dirty himself, nor should he allow the tools and equipment he uses to remain dirty longer than is necessary. It takes little time and effort to wipe tools clean during and after each job, and the cleaning itself leads to more care being taken of tools and of the work in hand.

Tidiness entails working to a logical and definite system during each job. The job then progresses smoothly from one stage to the next with less effort and with fewer delays. Accidental damage is reduced, tools are ready to hand, related parts are kept together, part locations are correctly marked and generally a pride is taken in performing a good job in a reasonable time. When the job is completed the floor or bench should be cleared and cleaned ready for the next job. An untidy man who works in a confused mess of tools, dirt, oil and parts is a poor advertisement for himself, his trade and his employer. It is far more pleasant and healthy to work in clean and tidy surroundings, and a well-ordered garage gives the impression of good craftsmen turning out a high standard of work.

**Time-keeping.** Time lost or wasted costs the garage charging time – money which should be coming in. Good time-keeping is an essential part of the duty of a mechanic to his employer. Work must start and finish on time throughout the working day.

**Skylarking.** Playing practical jokes must not be permitted in work-shops. Quite apart from the time wasted and ill feeling caused, it always results in someone being hurt or equipment being damaged.

Workshop rules vary between garages and are often never written down; mechanics are expected to understand the conditions and so behave in a reasonable and responsible manner.

A large number of accidents occur in factories and garages every day. About two-thirds of these are the fault of the individual employee, who may or may not be injured. More often than not such 'bad luck' is the result of ignorance, lack of care, over self-confidence, or the taking of unnecessary risks.

In garage work special dangers exist which must be recognized. Precautions must always be taken to reduce the possible chances of accidents happening. These precautions are generally only applied common sense – once the dangers are realized. The more important sources of danger, with their associated accidental injuries to operators, equipment and vehicles, are those concerning inflammable liquids, rotating machinery, lifting and supporting equipment, electrically-powered tools, and poorly ventilated workshops and pits.

**Inflammable Liquids**

The obvious danger from these is that of starting a serious fire. Petrol, cellulose paints and thinners, and a number of liquids used for cleaning and degreasing will all vaporize at normal temperatures. The vapour spreads quickly through the air and is very easily ignited by an open flame. It may even be ignited by the spark from a metal stud in a boot. The strong characteristic smell of these vapours should act as a warning of fire risk. The vapours should not be inhaled for long periods as some are poisonous while others irritate the eyes, nose and lungs.

*Precautions*
(1) Never permit an open flame or any source of direct heat to be brought into, or near, stores or workshops where these liquids are stored or exposed for use. Smoking must be strictly banned. If large quantities are stored special buildings or chambers must be used. Fire appliances must be readily available and kept in good order. In such shops and stores only rubber footwear should be used to reduce the chances of causing a spark.

(2) Never draw more supplies from the stores than can be used in the immediate future. Always replace container lids. Mop up spilled liquids at once and place the rags in a lidded bin.

(3) The vapours and spray from paint irritate the delicate linings of the nose, lungs, and stomach. Some paints are also poisonous. Always wear the mask provided. Don't take food into the spray shop. Don't eat in the spray shop. Outside the shop drink as much milk as you can to stop the paint injuring the stomach lining. Do not spray unless the air extractor fans are operating.

(4) When draining petrol tanks do not stay in the pit and do not breathe the fumes. Make sure the way out is quite unobstructed. Warn others not to smoke anywhere near the pit. Keep a fire extinguisher of the correct type near by.

(5) Do not use inflammable liquids on or near a vehicle when electrical equipment is being repaired.

(6) Know where all the fire appliances are. Keep them clear of obstructions. Learn the different types and their uses – there is no time to read instructions when a fire starts. Only immediate action can save lives and reduce the damage.

Two well-known types of extinguisher are illustrated in Fig. 1.1.

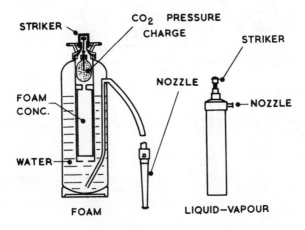

Fig. 1.1 Fire extinguishers

**Rotating machinery**

This includes all forms of rotating shafts, gears, pulleys and belts, and the exposed parts of all powered machines. A shaft may appear to be quite smooth, but when it is rotating at high speeds it will grab any loose material which comes into contact with it and wrap it tightly around itself. If the shaft is rough or has any projections such as splines, couplings, bolts or gear teeth the grabbing effect is even more violent.

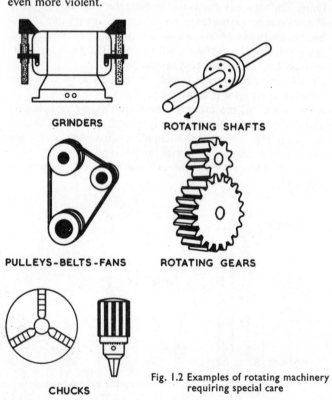

GRINDERS

ROTATING SHAFTS

PULLEYS-BELTS-FANS

ROTATING GEARS

CHUCKS

Fig. 1.2 Examples of rotating machinery requiring special care

**Precautions**

(1) Before using any form of powered machinery find out how it is stopped.

(2) Always switch off the power, or disengage the drive, before changing the gear ratios or belts, particularly of such equipment as drilling machines, lathes, flexible drive tools and boring bars.

(3) Keep the hands well clear of moving shafts and any exposed parts of moving machinery, particularly the cutter heads and spindles of drilling machines and boring bars, and the chucks and lead screws of lathes.

(4) Machines do not stop automatically because someone happens to be caught up in them. Do not wear clothing which flaps about and may become caught; neckties are a special menace. Do not try to pull cuttings clear of the work with the bare hands – use a metal rod or piece of stick. Wear proper overalls – these are a safety measure as well as protective clothing.

(5) Do not wear long hair. This is especially liable to be caught up by the spindles of drilling machines. Choose a short hair style or wear a cap which covers it when working. Finger rings and wristwatches can also be caught by the projections of rotating machinery.

Figure 1.2 illustrates examples of rotating machinery usually found in the workshop which can be dangerous if not treated with care.

### Portable electric tools

The larger and heavier electrically powered tools are installed as fixed equipment. The electric power can therefore be supplied to their driving motors through fixed cables which are protected from accidental damage by their enclosure in steel tubing. In garages such permanently connected machines include air compressors, car lifts, pedestal grinders, and pillar drilling machines.

In garages it is often necessary to take the tool to the job. Such tools must therefore be portable, and their power supply must be arranged temporarily for each job. This is done by the use of sockets and plugs, and tough, flexible, rubber-covered cables, but the use of such cables adds to the sources of danger in the workshop. Portable tools include drilling machines, valve and seat grinding tools, electric welding equipment, and electrical testing instrument sets.

## Electric shock

Electricity will always take the path which offers the least resistance to its flow. If electrical equipment has been roughly handled, causing wires to be exposed or switch parts loosened, the electricity may flow through the frame of the tool rather than pass through the motor, and complete its path to earth by passing through the body of the operator. This subjects him to a violent shock which is always very alarming, and often results in death.

## Connecting plugs

Plugs are used to connect the tool power supply cables to the main sockets, 240 volts alternating current being the usual mains supply. The plug is an insulated moulding of plastic or tough rubber which houses three strong brass pins and a cartridge type of fuse. The pins are engaged with three rectangular contact tubes in the socket box. The fuse is usually rated to carry 13 amps and will melt to break the circuit if an excessive load is passed, so protecting the tool. It is very important from the point of view of safety that the wires be correctly secured to their correct pins (Fig. 1.3). Although

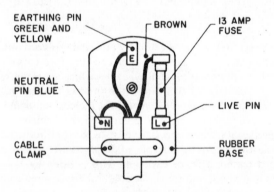

Fig. 1.3 Fused plug

a.c. current is employed the tool switch and the fuse must be in the same length of wire. This wire is termed the live, positive or feed wire and is coloured brown. It must be connected to the fused pin.

The return, neutral or negative wire is secured to the pin alongside the live pin and is coloured blue. The neutral pin is marked N and the live pin L. A third, green and yellow, wire is connected to the pin marked E. This wire connects the frame of the tool with the earth and provides an easy alternative path for the electrical current if either of the other wires should contact the frame of the tool – so reducing both the chances of the person using the tool receiving a shock and the size of the shock.

The tough rubber outer cover of the cable must be securely clamped into the plug and into the tool to stop any pulling of the current-carrying wires.

*Precautions*
(1) Remember that electricity cannot be seen and that you will have no advance warning of a shock.
(2) Do not pull tools about by their cables. Always arrange them so neither you nor others will trip over them. Do not allow them to be run over, trapped, or soaked in oil or water.
(3) Always check the cables at both ends for exposed wires and loose connectors.
(4) Always switch off at the socket before fitting the plug. See the machine switch is off before switching on the socket. Reverse the procedure when the job is completed.
(5) If the fuse blows examine the tool and cable carefully to establish the cause. If this is not obvious have the drill examined by an electrician.
(6) Avoid using portable electric tools while standing on wet floors. If this must be done, wear thick rubber boots.
(7) Check that the cable is suitable to carry the current needed to operate the tool.

**Emergency treatment**
When a person has been rendered unconscious as a result of an accident, he may have stopped breathing. *It is most important that he be given help at once.* A doctor must be sent for but his workmates must start the treatment immediately and not wait for the doctor. The treatment is a method of artificial respiration which gets the lung muscles working again to pass fresh, or oxygen-containing, blood to the heart and brain.

Take the patient into the fresh air and ease any tight clothing. Then lay him face down with his forehead on his folded arms, care being taken to keep his mouth and nose clear of the ground and his tongue forward in his mouth. Keep him warm with a coat or blanket.

In giving aid, kneel down, facing the patient's head, with one knee near his head and one foot near his elbow (Fig. 1.4). Then spread both hands, with the thumbs touching, upon the patient's shoulder blades, keeping both arms straight. By leaning forward until the arms are vertical, the body weight is exerted on the patient for 2·5 seconds (count 1000, 2000, 3000). Now slide the hands

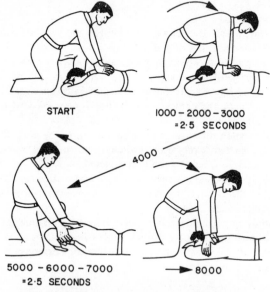

Fig. 1.4 Applying artificial respiration

under the patient's elbows to grip his upper arms (count 4000) and raise his arms and shoulders by rocking back, until resistance is felt (count 5000, 6000, 7000). The operation is completed by returning the patient's arms to the ground. Replace the hands upon the patient's shoulder blades (8000) and repeat the cycle to a rhythm of 9 times a minute.

Artificial respiration is very hard work but it saves lives. It must not be stopped until the patient is again breathing normally and the doctor has taken charge. It may even have to be continued in an ambulance on the way to the hospital. Relays of helpers may be needed in some cases. The change-over of helpers must be done smoothly and quickly.

## Dangerous Gases

Gases are used, and sometimes produced, as a part of the normal work carried out in garages. Their characteristics and the dangers associated with them must be taken into account at all times.

*Oxygen.* Oxygen has no smell and no colour, and it is slightly heavier than air. Combustion cannot occur without its presence and is greatly assisted if large quantities of oxygen are available. Oxygen is stored under high pressures (about $14000 \text{ kN/m}^2$) in strong steel cylinders or bottles. Because of the way it encourages combustion it must never be released into the air of the workshop. It must never be used in the place of compressed air and must never be allowed to come into contact with oil or grease.

*Acetylene.* This gas has no colour but has a strong and rather offensive smell. It is dissolved in acetone and is released as a gas when the steel storage bottle is opened. Acetylene is easily ignited by a spark or flame and burns with a yellow flame tinged with black smoke. When correctly mixed with oxygen, in a special nozzle, the mixture burns with a clean blue flame producing a temperature of between 3000 °C and 4000 °C.

*Hydrogen.* Hydrogen has neither colour nor smell and is very much lighter than air. It will burn very easily in air to produce a very hot and colourless flame. Mixtures of hydrogen and air will explode violently if ignited. Hydrogen is used mixed with oxygen in some welding operations. It is also given off by a car battery when the battery is being charged. Do not smoke near batteries on charge or an explosion may occur.

*Exhaust gases.* When rich mixtures of petrol and air are burned the exhaust contains both carbon monoxide and carbon dioxide gases. Both gases are colourless and free from smell. Carbon dioxide is heavier than air and will neither burn itself nor help combustion. Carbon monoxide is very poisonous and this is the main danger in exhaust gas. Engines should not be run in workshops or pits where the gases can collect to form a deadly concentration. Engines may be run only in the shop where the doors or windows are open. The first sign of this poisoning is a violent headache. This is followed by unconsciousness, and death will result if the victim is not taken into the fresh air and revived. Visible signs of this poisoning are a white face and blue lips.

*Compressed air.* In garage work compressed air has the greatest variety of uses. Ordinarily air is not dangerous, but at high pressures (usually 700 to 1400 kN/m²) it may be. Reinforced hoses and special connectors are used to convey high-pressure air; they must never be abused. An air hose in use exerts a considerable 'kick' which must be expected and controlled. Hoses must never be kinked to shut off the pressure. Compressed air must never be used to dust clothes nor used against the eyes, ears or other parts of the body. The misuse of compressed air in practical jokes has often resulted in very serious injury and even death.

*Coal gas.* This is heavier than air and is colourless. When mixed with the correct quantities of air in a burner it burns with a hot blue flame. When mixed freely with air the mixture will explode if contacted by a spark or flame. Coal gas is therefore given a strong and offensive smell which serves as a warning of its presence.

All hoses and pipes used to carry gases must be treated with care and not crushed, cut, stretched, or exposed to oil or heat. The proper connectors must be employed, together with the necessary valves. Hoses should be as short as is practicable and should be kept on reels until required.

### Identification of gases and liquids

The various liquids and gases employed in workshops can cause considerable danger if they and their containers are not treated carefully. It is important that their correct identification be made easily and quickly, and the British Standards Institute has recommended a system of pipe and container markings based on a colour code. The code consists of a basic or ground colour for a pipe with special band markings of a different colour. Examples are given in the Table 1.1., together with the BS colour numbers.

Table I.I.

| Pipe Contents | Ground Colour | Col. No. | Band Colour | Col. No. |
|---|---|---|---|---|
| WATER | | | | |
| Drinking | Aircraft blue | 108 | — | |
| Central heating (60 °C to 100 °C) | French blue | 166 | Post Office red | 538 |
| Hydraulic power | Mid-Brunswick green | 226 | — | |
| AIR | | | | |
| Compressed – up to 1400 kN/m² | White | | — | |
| Compressed – over 1400 kN/m² | White | | Post Office red | 538 |
| Vacuum | White | | Black | |
| STEAM | Aluminium and crimson | 540 | — | |
| DRAINAGE | Black | | — | |
| ELECTRICAL SERVICES | Light orange | 557 | — | |
| TOWN GAS | Canary yellow | 309 | — | |
| OILS | | | | |
| Diesel fuel | Light brown | 410 | — | |
| Hydraulic power | Salmon pink | 447 | Sea green | 217 |
| Lubricating | Salmon pink | 447 | — | |
| Furnace fuel | Dark brown | 412 | — | |
| FIRE INSTALLATIONS | Signal red | 537 | — | |
| GASES | | | | |
| Acetylene | Dark grey | 632 | Maroon | 541 |
| Oxygen | Dark grey | 632 | Black | |
| Coal gas | Dark grey | 632 | Red | 537 |
| Hydrogen | Dark grey | 632 | Red | 537 |
| Butane | Dark grey | 632 | Red | 537 |

Extract from BS 1710:1960 *Identification of Pipelines.*

**Lifting equipment**

This includes car lifts, screw, bottle and trolley jacks, cranes and hoists, axle stands and cradles (see Fig. 1.5).

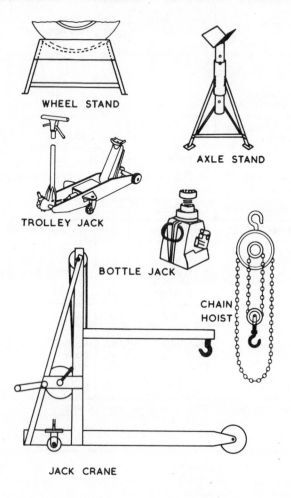

WHEEL STAND

AXLE STAND

TROLLEY JACK

BOTTLE JACK

CHAIN HOIST

JACK CRANE

Fig. 1.5 Examples of lifting equipment

*Precautions*

(1) Before raising any type of car lift, make sure the vehicle is centralized and that the wheels are properly chocked. Check that the vehicle doors are closed and so cannot foul any other vehicle or parts of the building. If the ceiling is low check that the vehicle cannot touch it when the lift is fully raised. If the lift is operated by compressed air check that the storage tank pressure is adequate.

(2) When the lift is raised, check that the automatic locks, designed to prevent or slow the accidental dropping of the lift, are correctly engaged.

(3) Work on the underside of the vehicle only should be carried out while the lift is raised. It is a most dangerous practice to work while standing on the ramps.

(4) When lowering the lift, first check that other mechanics, all tools and equipment are clear of the ramps and ramp pits. Guide the ramps carefully into their pits. Keep the legs and feet clear of the ramps at all times.

(5) Screw, bottle and trolley jacks must all be used only on firm ground. They should be checked for damage and oil leaks before being loaded. The collapse of a jack may well cause very serious injury to a mechanic, as well as resulting in extensive damage to the vehicle. The screw jack used in garages is a very powerful and strongly made tool which is not likely to collapse. The screw jack supplied with many cars, through less robust, is generally adequate for its purpose, providing that it is correctly fitted into its jacking sockets and is based on hard and level ground. The car wheels should always be chocked to prevent the car rolling as it is lifted. If it does roll the jacking brackets and the jack will be badly damaged and the user may be seriously hurt.

(6) Both the bottle and the trolley jack are hydraulically operated and are liable to collapse if they have been neglected or are overloaded. Never work under a vehicle which is supported only by these jacks. Apart from the possibility of a jack collapsing, a single trolley jack allows a vehicle to rock and it may slide off the jack platform. This is always possible when lifting by the centre of the rear axle. Use the jack solely to lift the

vehicle to the height needed to install axle stands or wheel cradles.

(7) Axle stands must be so positioned that they do not rock and have no tendency to allow the vehicle to slide on them. They should have a wide base and must only be used on hard and level ground. For many jobs wheel cradles are preferred as they are more rigid and have wider bases.

Cranes and hoists are usually hand-operated winches with varying types of jib. All have some form of self-engaging locking device, usually a pawl and ratchet, which enables the operator to wind or release the chain or cable under safe control. This mechanism, and the chains or cables, must be kept clean and free from rust. The safe working load must be clearly marked and must never be exceeded. It is a legal requirement that chains be heat treated at intervals, and records must be kept for examination by the Factories Inspector.

(8) Before lifting, check the locking pawl for correct operation. Check that the slings are secure and not likely to slip, and that they are padded where this is required to prevent damage.

(9) Take the weight slowly and be ready for the vehicle or unit sliding. Stop and check the security of the slings. If they are satisfactory complete the lifting operation.

(10) When lowering watch the slings carefully in case of slip. Lower carefully and slowly to the bench or ground. Check that the car or unit is firmly supported before allowing the slings to fall free.

# Irons and Steels

The metals used in the construction of the motor vehicle may be divided into two different groups. Those which contain iron are known as *ferrous* metals, while those which contain no iron at all are known as *non-ferrous* metals. Irons and steels are ferrous metals. Copper, lead, tin and aluminium are non-ferrous metals.

Pure iron is not used in engineering. It is very difficult to produce and very difficult to machine without tearing the surface. If small percentages of carbon are combined with the iron, however, the resulting metal becomes one of the many different varieties of iron and steel in common use.

*Note.* It is the percentage of *combined carbon* which determines whether the metal is called iron or steel. The amount of *combined carbon* also determines the properties of the metal and the processes by which it may be worked into its final shape and condition.

**Properties of metals**

The properties of a metal are those features which give it its own particular nature or identity. They determine the use which can be made of it and the processes by which it can be worked.

*Definitions*

Fusibility: the ability to flow easily when molten and, after cooling and solidification, to retain accurately the shape of the mould into which it has been poured.

Weldability: the ability to melt and fuse together at a point subjected to an intense local heat.

Ductility: the ability to be forced or drawn into a different shape without fracture.

Malleability: the ability to be beaten into a different shape without fracture.

Toughness: the ability to resist a change of shape although a change can be made without fracture when sufficient force is applied.

Hardness: the ability to resist penetration or a change of shape until fracture occurs.

Brittleness: resistance to change of shape to such an extent that fracture occurs before any change takes place.

Plasticity: the ability to change shape easily without fracture.

Tenacity: the ability to resist being pulled apart.

Elasticity: the ability to return to its original shape when the force causing a change of shape is removed.

Elongation: the amount of stretch produced between two fixed points, the stretch consisting of general stretch and a drawing out at the point of fracture.

*Strengths*

Tensile strength: the force required, in meganewton per square metre, acting along the axis, to pull the metal apart.

Compressive strength: the force required, in meganewton per square metre, to fracture the metal by crushing. Compressive strength is indicated by writing $MN/m^2$ *comp*.

Torsional strength: the force required, per unit of cross-sectional area, to cause fracture by twisting.

Shear strength: the force required, acting at 90° to the axis, to cause fracture by the sliding apart or cutting of the metal.

Stress: when an external force is applied to the metal a resisting force is set up in the metal to oppose it. This *internal resisting force* is called stress and is calculated by dividing the external force by the area of the cross-section of the metal.

Strain: this is the deformation produced in the metal by the action of stress.

## Processes in shaping metals

By 'process' is meant the method by which a metal is formed into its final shape and condition. Processes include both physical working and heat treatment methods, and these depend upon the properties of the metal.

*Physical working methods*

Casting: this is the pouring of a molten metal into a mould, usually of sand, which is of the final shape required (Fig. 2.1). When the

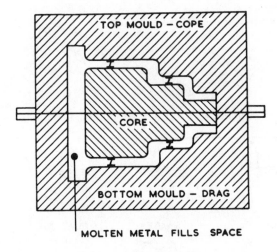

Fig. 2.1 Moulds for casting

metal has cooled and solidified the casting is removed and cleaned ready for the machining operations.

Die-casting: this is a special form of casting in which metal moulds are used and the molten metal is forced into the mould under pressure. The casting is removed when solid and is ready for machining. This is a mass-production method often used for small parts made from alloys of zinc, copper and aluminium.

Forging: the shaping of very hot metals by repeated hammer blows. Hand-hammered forgings are shaped on an anvil (Fig. 2.2) using various shaping tools as illustrated in Fig. 2.3.

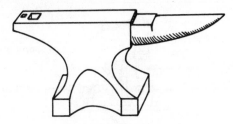

Fig. 2.2 Anvil

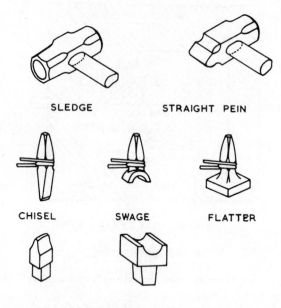

Fig. 2.3 Forging tools used on the anvil

Drop forging: a special type of forging using a machine hammer and shaped dies or anvils. A compressed-air-operated hammer is shown in Fig. 2.4. Typical dies and the method of producing a drop forging are illustrated in Fig. 2.5.

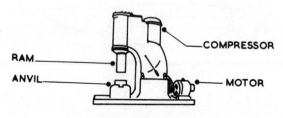

Fig. 2.4 Air hammer

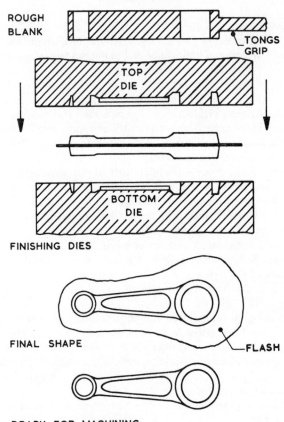

ROUGH
BLANK

TONGS
GRIP

TOP
DIE

BOTTOM
DIE

FINISHING DIES

FINAL SHAPE

FLASH

READY FOR MACHINING

Fig. 2.5 Drop forging produced from power hammer and dies

Pressing: the forcing of hot or cold metals into shaped die plates brought together under very high pressures.

Welding: the joining of metals of the same nature by local melting and fusing together. The heat may be obtained from an oxy-acetylene flame or from an electric arc.

Rolling: the shaping of heated metals by repeated passing through rollers or presses. This is generally done in steel mills to produce sheet, bar or tube from cast steel ingots.

*Heat treatments*

These treatments are carried out after the final shape has been obtained, in order to improve or add to the properties of the metal to make it more suitable for its purpose.

Hardening: this process is carried out on medium and high carbon content steels, and on alloy steels, to produce the maximum possible hardness right through the material. This process makes the metal very hard but also very brittle and much less ductile. For most purposes some of this excessive hardness must be reduced and the reduction is called tempering.

Tempering: this process is always carried out after hardening; it reduces the excessive hardness and brittleness, and increases the toughness of the material to enable it to resist shock loads. The higher the temperature during the tempering process the more the hardness is reduced and the tougher the material will be. Almost every tool is hardened and tempered, and in most of them the hardness and toughness varies at different points to suit the duty of each part of the tool.

Annealing: this process produces the softest possible condition in the material.

Normalizing: in complicated and large castings the different parts do not cool down at the same rates. Because of this, stresses are set up which cause the casting to alter its shape slightly as it ages. Pressings may also act in the same way. Both castings and pressings are normalized to reduce these stresses. Normalizing also produces a more even internal structure in the metal.

Case-hardening: this consists of two processes used to produce a very hard skin or 'case' on a part which has to resist surface wear and also shock loads. The first process adds carbon to the skin of a mild steel part. The whole part is then heat treated and the skin becomes very hard while the core remains softer and tougher.

Malleablizing: in this process some of the carbon is removed from the metal; usually cast iron is so treated. This allows a complicated shape to be cast in iron. After malleablizing such a casting is better able to resist shock loads.

## Pig iron

Iron is found in the form of an iron stone ore which contains about 40% to 60% of iron. The ore is smelted in a blast furnace to burn out the impurities and the crude iron produced is poured into moulds called *pigs*. Pig iron contains varying percentages of carbon, silicon, phosphorus and manganese. Generally the carbon present is in the form of graphite, or in a combined form called *cementite*. If the pig iron is cooled quickly the greater proportion of the carbon is in the cementite form and the iron is much harder. If the cooling is slow the greater proportion of the carbon is in the form of graphite and is not combined with the iron. This provides a softer metal which is darker grey in colour at a fracture. Pig iron is not directly suitable for engineering purposes. Further refining is essential.

## Cast iron

Cast iron is made by melting down pig iron and scrap in a cupola. While the iron is molten alloying materials are added in the correct proportions to produce the type of iron needed for a particular purpose. The total percentage of carbon in cast iron is about 3%.

The other alloying elements are:

Silicon: this helps the formation of the uncombined carbon or graphite which makes the iron softer and easier to machine. It also helps to produce a casting free from blow holes. Up to about 3% of silicon is generally required.

Phosphorus: this is always present as an impurity and is not always desirable. In cast iron it improves the fusibility, and also produces better castings where the shape is more complicated and delicate. About 0·1% of phosphorus is usually required.

Sulphur: this also is an impurity. It has the effect of making the iron harder and more difficult to cast. The sulphur content must be kept as low as possible but usually about 0·1% is present.

Manganese: this is similar in its effect to sulphur and up to about 1% is usually present.

As an example, the cast iron of a cylinder block is a grey iron containing 93·32% of iron, 3·3% of carbon, 1·9% of silicon, 0·8%

of manganese, 0·14% of sulphur and 0·18% each of phosphorus, molybdenum and chromium.

The carbon content of 3·3% consists of about 0·7% of combined carbon and about 2·6% of 'free carbon' or graphite.

*Properties*

Because of the free carbon, cast iron is soft and easy to machine. It is brittle but has a hard-wearing surface. It has little or no elasticity. Cast iron has a tensile strength of only about $155 MN/m^2$ but a compressive strength of about $620 MN/m^2$. Cast iron can be made harder only by the use of *chills*. These are metal shapes which are fitted into the sand moulds before casting. They absorb the heat more quickly than does the sand and so cool the metal more quickly at that point. This in turn produces in the iron a greater proportion of combined carbon (cementite) and therefore a very hard portion of the casting. Some flywheel faces may be chilled in this way to produce a very hard wearing surface. Such a surface can only be machined by grinding.

*How cast iron is worked*

By casting and machining. Castings of cast iron may be decarburized into malleable cast iron for gearbox and rear axle casings.

*Heat treatment of cast iron*

Normalizing relieves internal stresses set up by uneven rates of cooling. Castings are hardened by chills only.

*Uses*

Cast iron is used for those vehicle parts of complicated shape which are not subjected to tensile or shock loads, e.g. cylinder blocks and heads, water jacket elbows, piston rings. Some gearbox and clutch housings may be cast in cast iron and then decarburized into malleable iron which can resist shock loads. In the workshop cast iron is used for surface plates and, when chilled, for vee-blocks.

## Malleable cast iron

*Carbon content*

This is less than 1% and is all combined with the iron.

*Properties*
These are very similar to those of cast iron but malleable iron has about twice the tensile strength (310 MN/m$^2$) and can resist much greater shock loads.

*How malleable cast iron is worked*
It is first cast as cast iron and then decarburized. It is harder to machine than cast iron but easier than steel.

*Heat treatment of malleable cast iron*
Malleable cast iron can be neither hardened nor softened.

*Uses*
It is generally used as a substitute for the more expensive steel castings where its lower strength is still adequate. Examples are the various gear cases and dumb irons.

Note that malleable iron should not be welded. The weld may appear sound but will be very weak. Always repair by means of bronze welding.

## STEEL

The most important difference between the irons and the steels is the carbon content and its distribution. If all the carbon present is combined with the iron the metal is a steel. If the carbon content includes free graphite then the metal is an iron. When the carbon content (combined) exceeds about 1·5% the material changes from a steel to an iron.

When making steel, the basic material first produced is an impure iron. This is refined in a Bessemer converter to produce an almost pure molten iron. The correct percentages of carbon are then added to the iron to make the type of steel required. These would be known as *plain* or *straight carbon* steels. If extra properties are required for certain purposes then the necessary alloying materials are added at the same time as the carbon. The resulting steels are then known as *alloy steels*.

## Mild steel
*Carbon content*
Mild steel contains from 0·15% to 0·3% of carbon combined with the iron.

*Properties*
Mild steel is ductile and malleable. It is harder and tougher than most irons. The tensile strength is between 430 and 495 $MN/m^2$.

*How mild steel is worked*
Mild steel is easy to machine, and easy to weld, forge or press into a new shape. It may be worked hot or cold.

*Heat treatment of mild steel*
This metal, due to its low carbon content, can only be case hardened.

*Uses*
Mild steel is only suitable for parts subjected to low stresses, and where ductility and ease of forming are needed. Examples are body and chassis sections and panels, nuts, washers, some rivets, wheels and low-stress bolts.

**Medium carbon steel**

*Carbon content*
The carbon content of the medium steels varies from $0.35\%$ to $0.5\%$.

*Properties*
These are similar to those of mild steel but the medium steels are harder and tougher. They are also less ductile and less malleable.

*How medium steel is worked*
Medium carbon steels are worked in a similar manner to mild steels but with more difficulty. Hot working may be necessary.

*Heat treatment of medium carbon steel*
Medium steels can be hardened right through by hardening and tempering.

*Uses*
Uses are generally similar to those of mild steel, but medium steel is used in preference to mild steel where the stresses imposed are greater.

## High carbon steels

High carbon steels may be divided into two main groups. An old classification is that of tool steel and cast steel.

## Tool steel

This is a steel which contains from $1\cdot2\%$ to $1\cdot4\%$ of carbon. It is made in a crucible furnace. It is very tough and is always hardened and tempered. It will give a very fine cutting edge when carefully ground. It is used for some lathe tools, drills, milling cutters and surgical instruments. Because its manufacture is a slow and small-quantity method this steel is more expensive than most.

## Cast steel

Cast steel is not cast into its final shape. In this instance the term 'cast' refers only to the fact that the steel was cast into an ingot at the end of its manufacture. The shape required is produced by forging, rolling or machining.

Steel castings are made from a special form of mild steel.

### Carbon content

The carbon content of high carbon steel varies from about $0\cdot7\%$ to about $1\cdot2\%$.

### Properties

High carbon steels are very tough and fairly hard.

### How cast steel is worked

High carbon steels are hot rolled from ingots into plate, bar, sheet or tube. This steel is difficult to machine, and can only be efficiently machined by the use of tipped tools which are extremely hard and capable of having a very fine cutting edge. High carbon steels are difficult to weld.

### Heat treatment of cast steel

These steels are usually hardened right through by hardening and tempering.

*Uses*

High carbon steels are used for most tools and are hardened and tempered as required for their uses. More often than not these steels are used today as the basic material for the manufacture of alloy steels. Cast steel is used for files, drills, reamers, cold chisels and some vices. Vice bodies are not heat treated as these require a very tough but not hard material.

## High-tensile steel

This is any high carbon steel which has a tensile strength of over 770 MN/m$^2$. The increased strength is obtained by cold rolling or other work-hardening process and not by the use of alloying materials. High-tensile steel is used for very highly stressed parts such as main and big-end bearing bolts, cylinder head studs and spring U-bolts.

## High-speed steels

These are alloy steels which have been developed to enable them to take faster and heavier cuts without their cutting edges being softened and blunted.

## Uses of materials

Table 2.1 illustrates the materials from which various vehicle parts are made.

## Alloying materials

These are added to plain high-carbon steel during its manufacture to improve its existing properties or to add new properties. Although alloy steels are more expensive their use is fully justified by their extra strength and other properties which make them better suited to particular duties than the plain steels – so much so that there is hardly any plain steel used in the modern car. Alloy steel parts have a longer life and, for the same strength, weigh less. *Nickel* is used in steel making to improve strength and ductility. In mild steel it helps the case-hardening process by toughening the core and by making the skin less liable to chipping. Generally additions of up to 5% of nickel increase the toughness and the tensile strength.

Table 2.1 Uses of materials

| PART | MATERIAL | CONDITION |
|---|---|---|
| Cylinder block | Grey cast iron | Stress relieved |
| Cylinder liner | Chromium iron | Gas-hardened |
| Pistons | Cast iron or aluminiun alloy | Low-temperature stress relieved |
| Connecting rods | Nickel chrome steel | Hardened and tempered |
| Crankshaft | Nickel chromium molybdenum steel | Hardened journals and crankpins |
| Gudgeon pins | Mild (4% nickel) steel | Case-hardened |
| Valves | Nickel chromium steel | Toughened |
| Valve guides | Cast iron Aluminium bronze | Chilled |
| Camshaft | Nickel steel or alloy cast iron | Flame-hardened or chilled |
| Main and big end bearings | White metal or lead bronze | |
| Flywheel | High-grade cast iron or mild steel | Chilled case-hardened clutch face |
| Sump | Mild steel or cast aluminium alloy | |
| Stub axles and track arms | Chromium steel | Hardened and tempered |
| Half-shaft | Chromium molybdenum steel | Hardened and tempered |
| Gears | Nickel chromium steel | Case-hardened |
| Road springs | Silicon manganese steel | Hardened and tempered |

*Chromium.* The addition of chromium increases both its hardness and toughness, so adding to its wear-resisting qualities.

Nickel and chromium are usually both added to the steel. After hardening and tempering the nickel chrome steels are used for very highly stressed parts such as crankshafts. Stainless steels contain more than 12% of chromium.

*Vanadium* increases resistance to fatigue. Steels containing about 0·2% of vanadium are very tough and have a very high degree of elasticity. They may be used for axle beams and springs.

*Molybdenum* increases toughness and hardness at high temperatures. It is often used with nickel and chromium.

*Manganese* also increases toughness, especially where the hardness required is produced by rolling operations.

*Silicon,* used with manganese, improves the hardening process. Silicon manganese steel which has a silicon content of 1·5% is sometimes used for road springs and engine valve springs.

*Tungsten* improves the hardness of steel at high temperatures. Contact-breaker points are tipped with tungsten. Some engine valves and seat inserts are made from tungsten steels.

*Note.* Almost every part of the vehicle is made from one of the alloy steels. Each has been given a heat treatment to develop its own properties to suit the loads imposed upon it. *Heat must not be used during repairs or the heat treatment will be destroyed. The strength of the part may be reduced to such an extent as to cause either serious damage or a serious accident.*

### Workshop identification of metals

For most practical purposes the common irons and steels may be identified by the results of the simple tests shown in the following table.

Table 2.2  Identification of metals

| METAL | Visual inspection | Grinding | Filing | Drilling | Bending and breaking (Saw half-way and give a hammer blow) |
|---|---|---|---|---|---|
| | | | TESTS AND RESULTS | | |
| Cast iron | Dark grey. Rough finish. Probably mould joint line visible | Short stream of red sparks. Very occasional bright sparks | Hard skin, then easy to file. Graphite in cuttings | Easy to drill after scale is penetrated. Soft and granular cuttings. Graphite released | Breaks before bending |
| Mild steel | Dark blue scale. Smooth finish | Stream of long white sparks | Scale less hard and thicker than that of cast iron. Cuttings and surface silver | Easy to drill. Silvery spiral cuttings | Bends and breaks |
| Medium steel | Blue-black scale. Smooth finish | Wider stream of long white sparks. Occasional very bright sparks | Harder to file than mild steel | Harder to drill than Mild steel. Spiral silvery cuttings turning brown or blue | Bends slightly before breaking |
| High carbon steel (cast steel) | Polished black scale | Still wider stream of long white sparks – with patches of very bright sparks | Harder to file than medium steel | Harder to drill than medium steel. Cuttings break as they clear the drill | Resists bending and then breaks |
| High-speed steel | Rougher than the cast steel. Often painted | Stream of dull red sparks | Harder to file than mild steel but easier than cast steel | Fairly easy to drill. Long spiral cuttings | Resists bending and then breaks |

# 3    Solders and Fluxes

Joints may be classified as either permanent or temporary. Permanent joints are made by the use of heat or by the deformation of the metal. In most cases the jointing process has to be repeated when repairs become necessary. Examples of permanent joining methods are: soldering, brazing, welding, riveting and rolling.

Temporary joints are those which are intended to be released and remade, without damage, when required. Examples of temporary joints are those between the cylinder block and head, between the brake drum and the wheel hub, and between the engine and the clutch housing. In the last instance dowels are used to ensure accuracy of alignment between the two units. The most common fastening device used in the making of temporary joints is the nut and bolt or nut and stud.

**Soldering**

Soldering is a low-temperature, heat-joining method in which two surfaces are coated by a film of solder, heat and pressure being used to merge the two films into one to form the joint. *Solder* is an alloy of lead and tin which has a melting point of about 220 °C. Steels, tinned plate, brass and copper may be joined by this solder while other metals require their own special solders and fluxes. *Fluxes* are materials used to reduce or remove the oxides which form on heated surfaces and prevent the solder obtaining a good grip upon the surface.

**Solders.** Lead/tin solders are all classed as soft solders; i.e. low-melting-point solders to distinguish them from hard or high-melting-point solders which are used in higher temperature joining operations. Soft solders are sub-divided into three main groups of solder varying in their composition and melting points. These are:
(a) Fine or soft solder which contains 40% lead and 60% tin, and has a melting point of about 165 °C.

(b) Tinmans or medium solder which contains 50% lead and 50% tin, and has a melting point of about 190 °C.

(c) Hard solder which contains 60% lead and 40% tin, and melts at about 220 °C.

The melting point of lead is about 320 °C and that of tin about 230 °C, so the greater the proportion of lead the higher the melting point of the solder. Note that the solders have a lower melting point than the metals used to make them. Many solders also have small percentage additions of antimony or bismuth which makes them flow better.

Radiator cores are often manufactured by the use of hard lead/tin solders so repairs may be safely carried out by the use of soft solders.

**Fluxes.** It is most important that the solder film should penetrate the pores of the metal surfaces to obtain the maximum adhesion or grip. The surfaces must be clean and dry before the solder is melted and applied to them but they will be attacked by the oxygen of the air when they are heated to make the solder flow. This results in the formation of metal oxides on the surfaces which the solder cannot penetrate. The flux is used to keep the air away from the surfaces, to reduce the amount of oxidation taking place and to destroy the oxides by chemical action.

Fluxes are made in liquid, paste and powder form. Liquid fluxes for use with lead/tin solders are made by dissolving zinc in hydrochloric acid, zinc being added until no more zinc will dissolve. This flux is sometimes referred to as 'killed spirits'. Acid fluxes are very corrosive and must therefore be used only where the joint can be thoroughly washed after its completion. Paste fluxes are made from resin, turpentine and Vaseline, and these operate mainly by keeping the air away from the surfaces. Paste fluxes are not corrosive and should therefore always be used for work which cannot be washed after completion of the joint. Some modern soldering pastes consist of flux and powdered solder. These are very easy to apply to clean and dry surfaces and are non-corrosive.

Fluxes used for lead work consist of tallow and resin.

*Examples*

Soldered joints are not very strong and must therefore be made only in situations where there is very little stress, heat or vibration.

Soft solders and paste fluxes are used in radio and electrical work, examples being in radio set wiring circuits and in the commutators of starters and dynamos.

Medium solders and acid fluxes are used for general, tinsmith and light patching work.

Hard solders and acid fluxes are used in the construction of radiators and for body filling. In the latter solder is being replaced by fibre glass and slate powders in special resins. These are much easier and quicker to use and do not corrode.

### Soldering methods

The joint to be soldered must be close fitting and the surfaces must be dry and perfectly clean. *All* traces of oil and dirt *must* be removed by filing, scraping, emery cloth or sand. Note that emery cloth should not be used for soft metals like copper unless the surface is subsequently scraped all over. This is because particles of emery become embedded in the surface and prevent the solder adhering properly. Very large areas may be cleaned by immersing in an acid bath.

The cleaned and dry surfaces are then covered with liquid or paste flux, depending on the nature of the joint, and 'tinned'. Tinning is the name of the process by which the surfaces are initially coated with a thin film of solder.

### *Tinning*

Solder may be applied to the surfaces either by means of a copper bit known as a soldering iron or by melting solder on to the joint with a clean flame. If the iron is used it must first be tinned by heating in a flame, dipping in flux and rubbing in solder. The tip of the iron must be filed clean before it is tinned and it is important to heat the body of the copper bit and not only the tip. Once tinned the iron is used to melt solder from the stick on to the surface, and then to spread the solder thinly over the surface – the heat flowing from the iron to the surface rendering the solder molten and the movement of the iron displacing the flux before it. Types of soldering iron are shown in Fig. 3.1.

When a flame is used the solder is spread by means of a wiping pad or a brush dipped in flux.

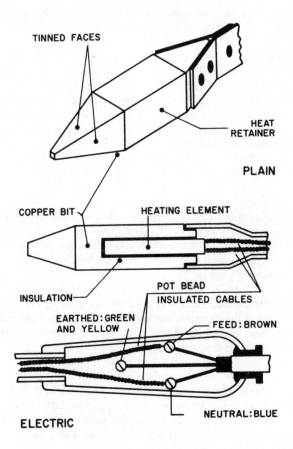

Fig. 3.1 Types of soldering iron

*Joining*

Once tinned the surfaces are wiped clean and covered again with fresh flux. They are then placed in their correct positions and, if possible or necessary, clamped. Heat (and pressure if possible) is applied to the joint by means of the freshly tinned iron or directly from a clean flame. (A clean flame means one free from smoke.)

The heat runs the two solder films into one to join the parts together.

### Hard soldering

This term includes silver soldering and brazing. The operations are similar to soft soldering in so far as two surfaces are joined by the addition of a third which adheres to them both. Different solders and fluxes are used and the operation is carried out at higher temperatures. Hard-soldered joints are much stronger than soft-soldered joints and they can resist much more stress, heat and vibration. Like soft-soldered joints the surfaces must be clean and dry and fit closely together.

*Silver soldering*

The solder used is an alloy of copper, silver and zinc which melts at between 600 °C and 750 °C. The flux used is borax powder mixed with water to form a paste. A better flux, called Boron Compo, can be bought. This is free from the bubbling which sometimes occurs with borax.

The parts to be joined are cleaned and clamped together after pasting with the flux. Heat is applied by means of a blowlamp or gas torch until the parts are red hot. The solder is then applied to the joint and melted in. When cool the flux powder must be brushed away and the joint washed.

*Brazing*

This provides a stronger joint than silver soldering and is carried out at temperatures of about 900 °C. The method used is similar to that of silver soldering but the solder used is called 'spelter'. Spelter consists of an alloy of copper and zinc. Occasionally tin is added. The flux used is Boron Compo.

Because of the extra heat required it may be found necessary to surround the work by fire bricks and to use a torch which can supply a greater quantity of heat, e.g. a gas and compressed-air torch.

Fuel and oil pipe unions should be silver soldered and not soft soldered. It is important to remember that the solder used must melt at much lower temperatures than the metals being joined. Care must always be taken to avoid the overheating of the parts.

# 4    Fitting Tools

**Hammers**

A large variety of hammers is available to meet the needs of different trades (see Fig. 4.1). Hammers are classified by their weight and by the shape of their *pein*, the pein being the end of the head opposite from the striking face. The head is usually forged from a 0·6% plain carbon steel and the faces are hardened and tempered while the centre is left soft. The shaft should be of straight-grained ash or hickory wood, and be suited to the head. The head must be securely attached to the shaft by a wedge of steel or hardwood.

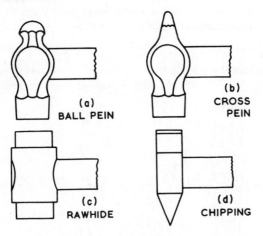

Fig. 4.1 Hammers

*Ball pein hammers*, Fig. 4.1(a) are generally the type most used by motor mechanics. A 0·1 kg hammer is needed for light work such as cutting paper gaskets or fitting cotter pins. A 0·45 kg or 0·70 kg hammer is suitable for most general work while heavier work, such as cutting out chassis rivets, is best done by the use of a 1 kg hammer. On rare occasions a 6 kg sledge may be needed.

Panel-beating work requires special hammers which are light in weight and have a square and a round face. These are used with metal blocks called 'dollies' and their faces must never be damaged by their misuse as ordinary hammers.

*Soft hammers* are needed to protect certain parts which must be hammered. These have replaceable faces of rawhide, Fig. 4.1(c) or copper. Rubber mallets are also very useful for such work.

Other trades use straight and cross pein hammers, claw hammers and pick hammers.

*Precautions*
(1) Choose the correct weight and pein of hammer for the job.
(2) Check that the head is securely fixed to the shaft and that the shaft is sound.
(3) Never use a steel hammer on shafts, threads or bearings.
(4) Never use a hammer if it is possible to use a press.
(5) Check that the workpiece cannot move.

### Chisels

The chisel is a cutting tool and is made from cast or tool steel (see Fig. 4.2). The cutting edge is hardened and tempered while

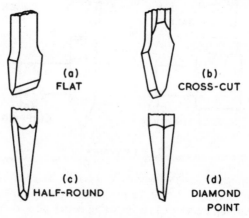

(a) FLAT

(b) CROSS-CUT

(c) HALF-ROUND

(d) DIAMOND POINT

Fig. 4.2 Chisels

the body is left softer and tougher. Chisels are made in different widths of cutting edge, and in different lengths. The cutting angles are varied to suit the nature of the material being cut. The four main types of chisel are:

**(1) The flat chisel.** This is used for cutting sheet metal, bolts and rivets, and for chipping large surfaces. It is usually about 180 mm to 200 mm long and may be of rectangular or octagonal cross-section. It is tapered and flattened for about one third of its length to form the cutting end. The cutting edge is usually ground to an angle of 60° and should be slightly curved. The very sharp corners at the ends of the edge should be removed.

**(2) The cross-cut chisel.** This is used for cutting or clearing keyways and slots, and in positions where a flat chisel cannot be used. Its cutting end is forged to an arrow-head shape and tapers down in thickness back from the cutting edge.

**(3) The half-round chisel.** This is used for cutting or clearing grooves. The cutting end is conical and has a flat on its upper surface. The cutting face is ground at an angle to the flat to form a semicircular cutting edge.

**(4) The diamond point chisel.** This can be used for grooving but is more often used in rectifying the incorrect location of the start to a drilled hole (drawing the drill).

## The hacksaw

Hacksaws are used to cut metals and other hard materials up to about 13 mm thickness. The blades are thin strips of carbon or alloy steel having a series of teeth cut in one edge (see Fig. 5.4). Holes are drilled through each end of the blade which fit over pegs in the tubular or bar type of saw frame. The frame has either a plain or pistol-grip handle and a blade tensioning device. The blade teeth only may be hardened and tempered or the whole blade so treated. The teeth are given a 'set' (are bent alternately to each side), to provide a clearance in the cut, i.e. the cut is wider than the blade. Blades are specified by the number of teeth per 25 mm, or pitch. The best all round pitch is 16–18 teeth per 25 mm, the pitch governing the work to be done by a given blade. The rule should be that there are never less than three teeth cutting at any time so thin sections and tubes should be cut by a fine-pitch blade, e.g. 32 teeth per 25 mm.

Steel rods and bolts should be cut by a 24-pitch blade, and solid brass, copper and cast iron by a 14-pitch blade.

The blade must be stretched taut between the pegs of the frame; slow, determined cuts should be used. The pressure should be applied only on the forward and cutting stroke and the blade lifted on the return stroke. A light pressure only must be used on tubes and thin sections of metal.

*Precautions*
(1) Check that the blade is fitted the right way round (with the teeth pointing forward) and is correctly tensioned; also that it is suitable for the work being done.
(2) Do not try to cut too fast; about 30–40 cuts per minute is reasonable.
(3) Do not use excessive pressure.
(4) Give the blade time to clear the cuttings.
(5) Do not twist or turn the blade.
(6) Use the full length of the blade on every stroke.

**Tin shears**

Tin shears or snips are used to shear or cut thin sheet metal and are made with straight or curved blades. Straight-bladed shears are used for straight cuts and for a large external radius. Curved-bladed types are used for cutting an internal curve or for trimming the end of a sheet metal cylinder. The blades or jaws are riveted together and may be sharpened by rubbing on an oil stone, care being taken to remove the least possible amount of metal from the flat side faces. There must be no gap between the blades as they close, a good test being to cut a piece of thin paper. If the cut is clean the shearing action will be satisfactory.

Heavier gauges of sheet metal and rods of up to 10 mm diameter may be cut by bench shears or a shearing machine. In this machine the blades have a parallel movement and the force from the long tubular lever is magnified at the blades.

*Precautions*
(1) Do not try to cut metal which is too thick by using tubes on the blade handles. This will ruin the blades and bend or break the handles.

(2) Use the shearing holes only for rods.

(3) Watch out for the very sharp edges of the cut metal.

(4) After using the bench shears dismantle the operating lever.

## Scrapers

Scraping is a method of removing very small quantities of metal from an irregular surface to make it level or regular, i.e. to remove the very slight high spots. A flat surface is checked by rubbing it very lightly over a surface plate covered by a very thin film of marking blue. The high spots are shown up by the blue being transferred from the surface plate, and are removed by very careful scraping – the art being to remove only the metal of the high spot. It is a trial and error process which requires a light and accurate touch and a great deal of patience.

In these days of fine finished bearings there is little real scraping work to be done, as far as vehicle parts are concerned. It may be necessary in trueing-up a bruised joint face or the bearings of some very large engines in which hand-fitted bearings are still used.

**Flat scrapers**, Fig. 4.3. These are rectangular in section and are

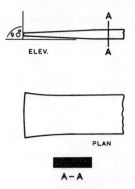

Fig. 4.3 Flat scraper

forged to spread the cutting end. The end is ground at 90° to the axis and is given a fine cutting edge by careful rubbing on an oil stone. The edge should be slightly curved and is rubbed on the stone in such a way as to rock along the curve, the flat sides also being rubbed to obtain a really sharp corner. The cutting action should be carried out by a circular pushing movement. Very good flat scrapers can be made from old files as the scraper must be as hard as possible to get a fine edge.

**Half-round scrapers.** These are used to correct cylindrical surfaces, usually the half-bearings of larger engines. In this operation the high spots are marked by blueing the shaft and rotating it in the assembled bearing. Once again great care and patience are required, and a good deal of time.

The half-round scraper is tapered and curved, and the under side is hollow ground to form a sharp cutting edge where it meets the flat edges of the curved portion (see Fig. 4.4). The cutting edges are sharpened by rubbing on an oil stone.

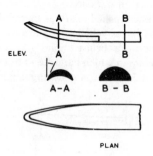

Fig. 4.4 Curved scraper

*Precautions*
(1) Use very lightly and carefully, removing metal only from the high spots.
(2) Keep the cutting edges very sharp.
(3) Do not try to rush the job.
(4) Keep the scrapers in a special box or leather guard; the edge must never be struck by other metal.

**Reamers,** Fig. 4.5

Reamers are used to bring a drilled hole to an exact size, to make it circular and parallel, and to provide a good surface finish. They are also used to true a bush after it has been pressed into place. It is important to remember that a reamer cannot correct the alignment of a hole already made.

Reamers are made from alloy steel and are then hardened and tempered and ground to size. The body is left softer and tougher and has a squared end for fitting the stock used to turn the reamer.

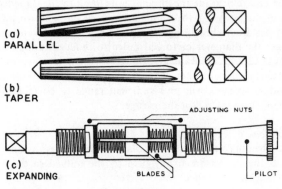

(a)
PARALLEL

(b)
TAPER

ADJUSTING NUTS

(c)
EXPANDING

BLADES

PILOT

Fig. 4.5 Reamers

It is important that the reamer be turned in one direction only during both entry and withdrawal, otherwise cuttings become locked and will damage the fine cutting edges. There are many different types of reamer to suit different jobs and various methods are used to operate them. In the garage the hand types of both solid and expanding reamer are used.

**Solid reamers.** These are usually cylindrical and have a slight taper to provide easier starting. They will not remove more than about 0·15 mm of metal. Taper reamers are also available for preparing drilled holes for taper-type cotter pins.

**Expanding reamers.** A very large stock of solid reamers would be required to enable a garage to ream bushes to suit every size of pin used in motor vehicles. The solid reamer also loses its accuracy after a certain amount of wear. These are the reasons why garages use the expanding types of reamer although they are not as strong as the solid types.

The expanding reamer consists of a grooved cylindrical body which is threaded at each end of the grooves. The grooves are deeper at one end and the body is extended to form a plain cylinder upon which is carried a sliding sleeve with a tapered outer surface. This sleeve acts as a pilot or centralizing device when two bushes must be cut on exactly the same axis, e.g. kingpin bushes in the steering stub axle. The cutting blades are fitted into the grooves and both ends of each blade are cut at an angle to engage with a similar angled cone cut inside the circular nuts fitted to the threaded portions of the body. As these nuts are moved up or down together, the blades are moved along the tapered grooves and so lifted up to increase the diameter or forced down to reduce the diameter. In this way a very accurate fit can be obtained to suit any slight variations in the diameter of the pin or shaft. A small selection of expanding reamers will give sufficient range to cover most jobs normally encountered in the garage.

*Precautions*

(1) Set the approximate starting diameter very carefully and check that the blades are firmly held by the nuts. Use the correct spanner size for these nuts.
(2) Remove any rough edges with a file before entering the reamer.
(3) Take only light cuts and clear the cuttings. Use a very thin lubricant only – oil and paraffin.
(4) Always use the pilot wherever possible.
(5) Turn in one direction, right hand, all the time. Never left hand.
(6) Never put the reamer down on the bare bench – always on soft material.
(7) Clean carefully after use. Oil and put back into the proper box or stand. The blades are very hard and sharp and are easily ruined or broken by a sharp blow.

**Punches**

Punches are made from cast steel and are hardened and tempered at the cutting or working end. The striking end is left softer and tougher.

**Centre punches** are used to make small circular marks or impressions to show the location of scribed lines. Where cutting operations of any sort are carried out up to the line it will be obscured by the slight roughness of the edge. The cutting is therefore continued until only half the centre punch mark is left showing. After marking out the hole by the use of dividers, centre-in the punch mark;

the centre is then punch marked more heavily to help the non-cutting point of the drill to clear the way for the lower part of the cutting edges to help the drill make an accurate start.

**Pin punches** are ground cylinders with flat ends. They are made in various diameters and are used to transmit the effect of a hammer blow into difficult positions.

**Hole punches** are used to make clean-cut holes in soft materials such as cork, gasket paper, and thin sheets of copper and aluminium. They are cylindrical in shape and are hollow for the lower part of their length. A cutting edge is ground at the bottom end either inside or outside the body. The material being cut must be supported by a piece of hardwood to avoid damaging the cutting edges, the displaced material eventually escaping through a hole in the side of the punch.

### Vices

One of the essential requirements of any form of metal working is a strong and rigid vice in which to hold the work. Vices may be classed as leg, bench, machine, or pipe types, while special vices are made to suit the requirements of particular purposes and trades.

**The leg vice.** This is a very strong and rigid type of vice which is particularly suitable for holding work which is to be hammered, chipped or bent cold. It may still be found in blacksmith and millwright shops. The leg is fastened into the floor, or supported on a block of hardwood, while the strap and fixed jaw attached to the leg are securely bolted to the bench top. The moving jaw is hinged on the leg and the jaws are kept apart by a strong flat spring. The moving jaw is forced inward by the action of turning a large square thread which is wound through a nut integral with the fixed jaw.

The disadvantage of this type is that the moving jaw travels in an arc. This results in the jaws never meeting squarely, and necessitates the use of very high pressures to hold the work firmly. This in turn leads to the distortion of the workpiece.

**The bench vice.** The parallel jaw vice was designed to overcome the disadvantages of the leg vice and although it is not quite so good for really heavy work it has replaced the leg vice for most purposes. Parallel jaw vices are made in two main forms, differing in their threads and speed of release.

**The plain vice.** This consists of a cast iron or cast steel body which is bolted firmly to the bench and carries the fixed jaw. The sliding jaw, of similar material, is accurately fitted to pass through the body and is secured by a large square thread. The thread also passes through a nut, which is dovetailed into the body, and a spring and cotter pin locate the handle end of the screw in the sliding jaw. The jaws are recessed for the fitting of serrated, hardened and tempered jaw plates which ensure a good grip on the workpiece. The jaw plates are held in position by countersunk machine screws.

The main disadvantage of this type is the time taken to move the sliding jaw.

**The quick-release vice.** Where a great deal of vice work is done a fair amount of time and effort can be saved by the use of the quick-release vice (see Fig. 4.6). In general arrangement it resembles the

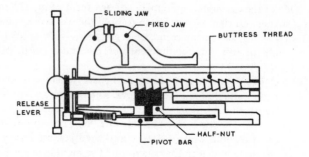

Fig. 4.6 Quick-release vice

plain vice but the screw has a buttress thread, and a half-nut engages with the lower half of the thread only. This half-nut is raised and lowered by the action of a flat bar which pivots about one edge. The bar is spring loaded to move the nut into engagement while a lever near the screw handle can pivot the bar in the opposite direction to release the nut. When the nut is released the moving jaw can be pulled out and pushed in quickly and the thread re-engaged to exert the gripping force. Although this is a popular type it has a shorter life than the plain type because of the inevitable wear on the half-nut.

*Vice specifications*

Vices are specified according to:

(a) The width of the jaws. Jaws of 65 mm to 200 mm are normally available but the 115 mm jaw is the most popular.

(b) The depth of the jaws. This is the distance between the top of the jaw and the top of the slide and varies with the jaw width. For a 115 mm jaw the depth is usually about 75 mm.

(c) The weight. The heavier the work to be carried out the stronger and therefore heavier the vice must be.

**Vice clamps** are special plates fitted over the jaw plates to protect light or accurately finished work from the hard serrations of the jaw plates. The gripping material may be of fibre, lead, tin plate or other soft material. Special shapes may be used for particular holding jobs, e.g. distributor bodies, and long shafts.

**Pipe vices** (Fig. 4.7) are specially designed to grip pipes which are to be cut to length or threaded. The sliding jaw is usually vertical and can be pivoted away from the fixed jaw. Both jaws are deeply serrated and the whole vice is much smaller and lighter than the bench vice. Folding stand and bench-mounted types are available.

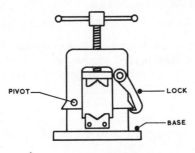

Fig. 4.7 Pipe vice

**The auto vice,** Fig. 4.8. This is designed for general garage use and is basically a plain vice which can be swivelled on its mounting plate and locked by screw levers. It has a small anvil and a cutting block formed on the back of the body which is cast steel. It also has detachable pipe vice jaws and a rod-cutting shear between and below the main jaws. These are deeply serrated and fibre vice clamps are supplied with the vice.

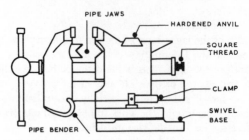

Fig. 4.8 Garage or auto vice

*Vice mounting*

The bench top, or front board, should be about 50 mm to 75 mm thick and about 400 mm wide. The front edge should be protected by flush-fitting angle iron. The top of the jaws should be about the height of the elbow of the person using the vice. The fixed jaw should project over the bench edge by about 12 mm to allow long pieces of material to be gripped vertically. The vice must be very firmly bolted to the bench.

*Precautions*

(1) Check that the vice is firmly bolted to the bench and that its jaw plates are tight in their recesses.

(2) Check that the jaw height is correct for you – stand on a block if necessary – good fitting work cannot be done if the position is wrong.

(3) Use vice clamps if necessary to protect the work.

(4) Do not overtighten the vice by the use of a hammer or a steel pipe.

(5) Do not hammer or chisel on the vice body unless provision has been made for this.

(6) Do not weld or braze in a vice – the heat will destroy the tempering of the jaw plates.

(7) Clean the vice properly after use. Oil the slides and the nut and thread at intervals.

**Machine vices** are parallel-jaw types designed to be clamped to the work table of machines. They are usually very rigid and flat and the long jaws may not be serrated.

**Hand vices.** It is often safer and more convenient to hold small workpieces in a hand vice during filing and drilling operations. These are either parallel or swinging jaw, or chuck types.

## Marking out

### Principles

When an engineering drawing is prepared all of the dimensions are based on centre lines and these have to be reproduced on the rough casting, forging or sheet of metal before the work of hand or machine finishing can be done. This reproduction is called 'marking out' and it must be done very carefully and accurately. Straight lines, angles, circles and curves may all be involved and their relative positions must also be accurately marked. The first principle of any marking out is that all the lines must be measured from one vertical and one horizontal base line or datum.

The lines are cut into the surface of the workpiece by the very hard and fine point of a scriber, chalk or acid copper sulphate being used to make the lines show more clearly. One line only must be scribed and if this is to mark a hand- or machine-cut edge it must also be lightly centre punched at intervals. The rough edge of the cut will obscure the line just as the final cut is due but the punch marks will remain visible. When finished to size the half punch marks should show as a check on the accuracy of machining. Holes for drilling should be marked by their centre, the diameters being lightly punched also.

### Marking-out tools

These may be classed as either locating or marking tools. Examples are shown in Fig. 4.9.

The locating tools are: surface-plates or marking-out tables, vee-blocks, slotted angle-plates, and tilting angle-plates. These are all made from cast iron and have very flat and rectangular surfaces. Vee-blocks are made of chilled cast iron; they are made and finished as pairs. The try-square is made of hardened and tempered high carbon or cast steel.

The *surface-plate* is a thick, rigid, and very flat plate which is used as the horizontal datum. *Vee-blocks* are rectangular with a vee-shaped recess in one side and are used on the surface-plate to support cylindrical work. *Angle-plates* are heavy and rigid and the workpiece may be clamped firmly to them on the surface-plate. The *try-square* is an 'L'-shaped tool which has two blades with exactly parallel sides, their edges being at 90° to each other and the

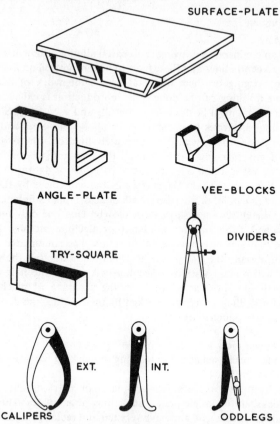

Fig. 4.9 Marking-out tools

thicker base. The try-square is used with feeler gauges to check the accuracy of right-angled corners, and with a scriber to mark out lines at 90° to an accurate edge.

The *marking tools* are of hardened and tempered high carbon or cast steel and include the scriber, scribing block, dividers, oddlegs, and centre punch. The *scriber* is a thin rod with very hard, fine-pointed ends which is used to cut the lines in the surface of the workpiece. The *scribing block* has an accurately-machined flat base with a vee-shaped recess, 2 retractable guide pins, and a pivoting pillar upon which is mounted a scriber with a hooked end. The pillar and the scriber can be clamped into any desired position. *Dividers* consist of a pair of very hard, pointed legs which are fastened together at one end, and are used to transfer measurements from a rule and to scribe circles and arcs. *Calipers* are used to obtain measurements between faces or of diameters of shafts. Internal calipers can measure diameters of holes and distances between internal faces. *Oddlegs* are similar to dividers but have one leg hooked and finishing in a rounded end. They are used to scribe lines parallel to an accurate edge, the hooked end being drawn along the edge. The *centre punch* used for marking has a finer point than that used for drill centring and is used to mark scribed lines which are the limits of a surface or edge.

*Precautions in use*
(1) Keep all marking-out tools clean and slightly oiled, and well away from all other tools.
(2) Take care to clean the tools and the workpiece before starting to mark out. Chalk or sulphate the surface of the workpiece.
(3) Handle the tools carefully – no knocking or rubbing of the surfaces.
(4) When transferring measurements from a rule, check that the point is fitted into the rule division accurately.
(5) Check that the clamps are tight on the scribing block.
(6) Centre punch very lightly and exactly on the lines and line junctions.
(7) Always work from one vertical and one horizontal base line.

*Method*
The uses of various marking-out and measuring tools are illustrated in Fig. 4.10.

When a workpiece is to be marked out it must be firmly clamped to an angle-plate on the surface-plate, or arranged firmly on the surface-plate, by packing pieces if necessary. The surface-plate is then used as the horizontal datum and all the horizontal lines scribed by means of the scribing block. The measurements are transferred from a steel rule of suitable length supported vertically by the clamp plate or a vee-block. Vertical lines may be scribed in a similar manner by turning the workpiece through exactly 90°,

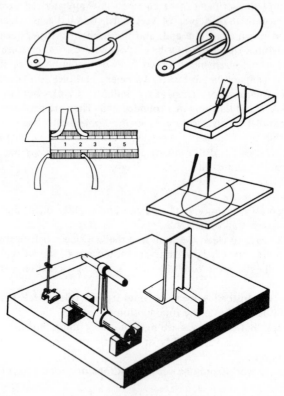

Fig. 4.10 Marking-out tools in use

or by using the dividers to space out the distances and the try-square to scribe the vertical lines from these. Cylindrical work may be marked in the same way when supported on the surface-plate in vee-blocks while keyways may be marked out by using the scribing block directly.

When marking out large areas of sheet metal trammels may be used instead of dividers. Trammels are beams of suitable length to which are clamped points like divider legs. These are usually capable of a fine adjustment and are used in conjunction with very long steel rules.

In vehicle repair work more checking of alignment is done than actual marking out, but small switch panels and templates are often required and the principles of marking out still apply. A 0·3 m steel rule, a scriber, dividers and oddlegs are still very useful tools for the motor mechanic.

## Files

Filing is one of the most important operations to be carried out by hand and a good fitter should be able to work to an accuracy of less than one-fifth of a millimetre with very little trouble.

### Construction

The file consists of a blade which ends in a tang to which the handle is attached. The blade is forged into shape from a billet of cast steel and is hardened and tempered after the teeth have been cut. The blade is therefore very hard and brittle but the tang is left softer and tougher.

### Classification

Although files are made in a great variety of shapes, to suit every requirement, they are classified mainly according to their length, their shape of cross-section, and to the type or cut of their teeth. The length dimension does not include the tang.

### Cut

There are four main types of file teeth cuts (Fig. 4.11). These are the single and the double cuts, and the dreadnought and the rasp. The first two are the ones used most often while the dreadnought is used for very heavy cutting. The rasp is used for the rough cutting of soft materials. Both of these are often replaced by the use of special-bladed tools such as the Surform range of cutting tools.

### Grade

There are slight variations between manufacturers in the numbers of teeth in each grade but the following is a fair guide:

Rough: used for fairly heavy roughing cuts to get under the skin of
   the metal – very coarse pitch teeth.

Bastard: for general use – coarse pitch.

Second cut: used to obtain a fair finish – medium pitch.

Smooth: used to obtain a better finish – fine pitch.

Dead smooth: used to obtain a very good, fine finish – very fine
   pitch.

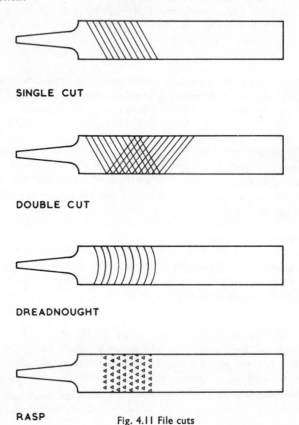

**SINGLE CUT**

**DOUBLE CUT**

**DREADNOUGHT**

**RASP**               Fig. 4.11 File cuts

The pitch of the teeth also varies with the length of the file, the
shorter the length the finer the pitch of the teeth.

In single cut files the teeth are parallel to each other and at an angle to the centre line of the file, the angle varying according to the material the file is intended to cut. The angle produces a slicing cut which removes the metal more easily than would be possible if the teeth were cut at right angles to the centre line. These files are used for very hard metals.

In double cut files a second set of teeth are cut over the first, and at a different angle. This produces small pyramid-shaped teeth which have more cutting edges. Double cut files are the ones in most general use, the first cut being at about 60° and the second at about 80° to the centre line.

The dreadnought file has curved teeth with a good self-clearing action, while those of the rasp are well-spaced and staggered triangular cutting points. The Surform blades are of thin, hardened and tempered steel which are somewhat similar to the domestic carrot grater, the material removed being passed through the perforated blade.

*Shapes*

Fig. 4.12 shows the shapes and sections of various files.

*Hand.* This file is parallel throughout its length, viewed from the cutting face, but its thickness or section tapers towards the end. Both faces are double cut and one edge is single cut. The other edge is left smooth and is called the 'safe edge'. This allows cuts to be made into corners without damaging the second surface.

*Pillar.* This file is the same as the hand file except that the faces are narrower. It is used where the hand file cannot be entered because of its width.

*Flat* files are tapered in both width and thickness and are double cut on both faces. Both edges are single cut.

*Warding.* These are similar to the flat files in shape and cut but are much smaller and thinner. They do not taper in thickness.

*Mill.* These are also similar to the flat file but are parallel in both width and section.

*Square* files are double cut on all faces and taper in section for the first third of their length. They are used to clear small corners and slots.

*Triangular.* These are double cut on all faces and are used to clear corners which are less than right angles.

*Knife edge.* This is a form of triangular file in which the angle between the faces is very small. Both faces are double cut and are bellied in side view. It is used in narrow vee-shaped slots and grooves.

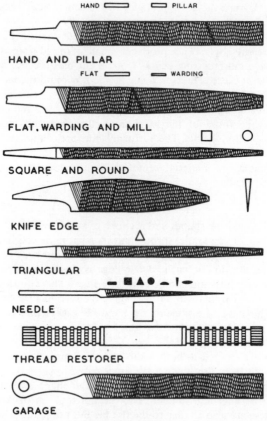

HAND □ □ PILLAR

**HAND AND PILLAR**

FLAT □ WARDING

**FLAT, WARDING AND MILL**

**SQUARE AND ROUND**

**KNIFE EDGE**

**TRIANGULAR**

**NEEDLE**

**THREAD RESTORER**

**GARAGE**

Fig. 4.12 File shapes

*Round.* Second cut and smooth round files are single cut while the rough and bastard grades are double cut. These are sometimes called 'rat-tail files' and taper in section for the first third of their length.

*Half round.* The flat face is usually double cut while the curved face may be single or double cut. The curved face is only part of a circle and may be used to cut radii.

Other files which may occasionally be used in garages are:

*Needle files* are very small files, of various shapes and sections, which are used for very fine and delicate work. The tang is formed into a long thin cylindrical shape and the pitch of the teeth ranges from medium fine to very fine.

*Thread files* are square section, double-ended files in which the faces are cut to form teeth of screw-thread form. Each file has a range of sizes of the more commonly used thread forms, and although they cannot cut a thread they are often most useful in dressing up a bruised thread.

*Garage files* are files in which the tang is forged into the shape of a flat handle.

*Magneto files* are small flexible files intended for use between contact breaker points. As coil ignition contact-breaker points are tipped with tungsten and not platinum they are almost as hard as the file. These files therefore cannot do the job as well as a fine carborundum stone.

*Precautions*
(1) Files are very hard and brittle. Do not drop them or throw them about or drop other tools upon them. Keep files in racks and avoid the chipping of the teeth which will result in poor quality workmanship.
(2) Select the correct file for the job in hand.
(3) Use new files for the softer metals first. This will prolong the life of the file as its teeth edges will not be dulled so soon.
(4) Always check that the handle is firmly attached to the tang. Failure to do so can lead to the tang being forced into the wrist.
(5) Check that the workpiece is firmly gripped in the vice. Set the working surface as close to the jaws as possible. Use vice clamps on machined surfaces and soft metals.
(6) Hold the file correctly and distribute the weight evenly over its whole length. Apply pressure only on the cutting strokes and do not allow the file to rock.

(7) File narrow surfaces diagonally.

(8) Use file card at intervals to remove chippings from the teeth. This will prevent the scoring of the working surface.

(9) Use chalk or paraffin to prevent 'picking up' when finishing the surface of the softer metals.

(10) Always remove sharp edges and tidy up the job.

### Screwdrivers, Fig. 4.13

Screwdrivers are made from cast steel and are hardened and tempered in such a way that the blade and edge are fairly hard but tough while the shank is less hard. It is most important that the handle should have a very firm grip upon the shank; the best screwdrivers for general garage use are those which have a tough, insulated, plastic handle. The blade must be so ground that it is a good fit in the slot of the screw and is not likely to slip. Screwdrivers are classified according to their purpose, blade length and blade width.

**Engineers' screwdrivers.** These vary in their length, width and section of blade. The sections are round or square, and the length may vary from 75 mm to 250 mm. Blade widths vary from 6 mm to 10 mm and are usually wider than the shank.

**Electricians' screwdrivers** vary in length also but the blade is always of the same diameter, i.e. the blade end is not wider than the shank portion. The shank may also be covered by an insulated sleeve and both the sleeve and handle are marked with the voltages they can resist. Small, pocket-sized versions of this type are also available. Screwdrivers with neon tubes incorporated are often useful to a mechanic doing a fair amount of electrical work.

**Ratchet screwdrivers.** In these a ratchet device is incorporated into the handle which allows the blade to be turned continuously, so speeding up the work.

**Spiral screwdrivers.** These are ratchet screwdrivers in which different sizes of blade may be fitted into a chuck on the end of an extension of the shank. This extension is of a relatively large diameter and has a number of spiral grooves cut into its outer surface. These pass through a nut inside the ratchet device in such a way that when the screwdriver is pushed down on to the screw the push is converted into a rotary motion. This turns the screw in or out according to the setting of the ratchet, the extension moving round as the handle moves down over it. These tools save a lot of time when large numbers of screws have to be fitted or removed.

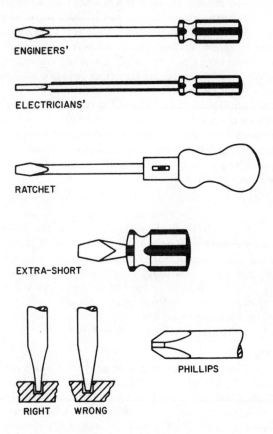

Fig. 4.13 Screwdrivers

*Special screwdrivers*

Very short screwdrivers are useful in the many restricted spaces on the vehicle. These have very short plastic handles and blades of 50 mm or less in length, although they are still about 6 mm in width.

Special screwdrivers are made for use with the Phillips type of screw head. In these the blade end is conical and has four grooves cut into it to form a star shape. The screw head has a similar shape of recess. The advantage of these screws is that a much more positive grip is obtained and the screw head is much stronger than that of the slotted screw. Various sizes of screwdriver are available to suit the different sizes of screw head. These are essential tools as the ordinary screwdriver cannot tighten or release a Phillips screw properly without damage.

Another very useful screwdriver is the type designed for use on hose clips of the Jubilee type. In these the blade is enclosed by a tubular guard which fits over the head of the worm or screw used to tighten or release the clamp band. This guard reduces the chance of the screwdriver slipping off the screw and possibly causing damage or personal injury.

*Precautions*
(1) Always select a screwdriver which is a good fit in the slot of the screw and which is as wide as the slot. At the end of the blade the sides should be approximately parallel to its centre line, a tapered blade causing the screwdriver to slip and injure the screw and the person using the screwdriver. The end of the blade should be flat and at right angles to its centre line.
(2) Never hammer a screwdriver and do not use it as a lever.
(3) Never use a screwdriver as a wedge between joint faces. These will be damaged or the blade will be broken.

**Pliers,** Fig. 4.14
Pliers consist of two jaws of cast or alloy steel which are forged into shape, and joined by a rivet, the jaws being hardened and tempered to enable them to cut and grip. Pliers are made in a great variety of shapes to meet the requirements of all trades. Those most suited to garage work include engineers' or combination pliers, side- or diagonal-cutting pliers, and long-nosed pliers. Special types which are of occasional use are the round-nosed, circlip, and cable-stripping pliers.
**Engineers' pliers.** These are made in various sizes and have parallel, serrated jaws with a pipe grip and, at the inner end of the jaws, cutting edges. A shear type of wire cutter is arranged at each size of the rivet.

**Side-cutting pliers** also are made in different sizes but can only be used for cutting cable, wire and pins of small diameter or soft material.

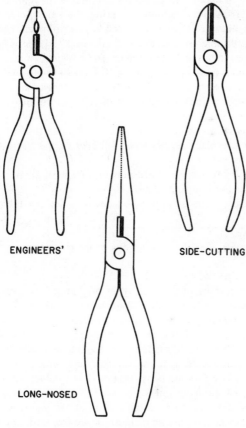

Fig. 4.14 Pliers

**Long-nosed pliers** have long, serrated and tapering jaws with cutting edges at their inner ends. They are useful in deep recesses where ordinary pliers cannot be used.

**Round-nosed pliers.** The jaws of these pliers are tapered cylinders without serrations or cutting edges. They may be used to form wire loops or to fit and remove very large circlips.

**Cable pliers.** There are a number of different designs of these pliers but all are so made that the action of bringing the handles together cuts and strips away the outer covering of an electrical cable.

**Slip-joint pliers** are sometimes called 'pipe-grip' pliers because one jaw has a double rivet hole which enables the jaws to be opened much wider than the normal pliers. These pliers can therefore grip pipes without crushing or slipping. The jaws are serrated and have a flat and a pipe grip. Some also have a shear cutting action. Slip-joint pliers are often supplied in vehicle tool kits.

*Precautions*
(1) Never use pliers on hardened surfaces or their serrations will be damaged.
(2) Never try to cut very hard pins or wire with pliers as this will splinter their cutting edges.
(3) Never use pliers on nut or bolt heads as the inevitable slipping will round off the corners and make them very difficult to remove.
(4) Never use pliers on pipe unions or die cast fittings.

**Spanners,** Figs. 4.15 and 4.16

A great number of different types of spanner are available and in time the motor mechanic will probably use them all. The main types of spanner are the open-ended wrenches, box wrenches or ring keys, combined ring-and-open-ended wrenches and sockets wrenches. These are all made in sets to suit the different sizes and forms of threads used in the various nuts, bolts, studs and set screws employed in the construction of the vehicle and its components. All good spanners are made from cast or alloy steel forgings and are designed to give years of service. It is false economy to buy cheap tools as these are made from inferior materials or are factory rejects.

**Open-ended wrenches** are double-ended and in stepped sizes, the openings being at about 15° to the centre line of the wrench. This allows the wrench to be used in restricted spaces; it is turned over to allow further movement of the nut or bolt. The length of a wrench is determined by the leverage required to tighten correctly its particular size and form of thread. Short and cranked open-ended wrenches are often most useful in very restricted spaces.

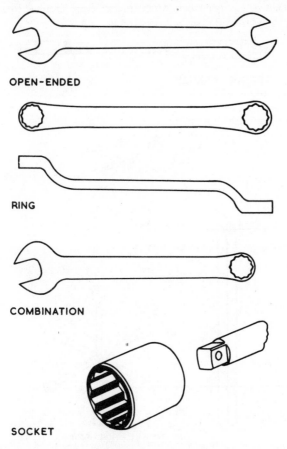

OPEN-ENDED

RING

COMBINATION

SOCKET

Fig. 4.15 Spanners and wrenches

**Ring keys.** These also are doubled-ended in stepped sizes but the ring ends are usually on the centre line. The holes are usually bi-hexagon in shape, i.e. they have twelve corners, and prevent slipping by fully surrounding the nut or bolt head. There are also single-hexagon wrenches. These are not always the best in restricted spaces but are less likely to take the corners off a damaged or corroded nut. Most ring keys are cranked to enable them to be used on partly recessed nuts.

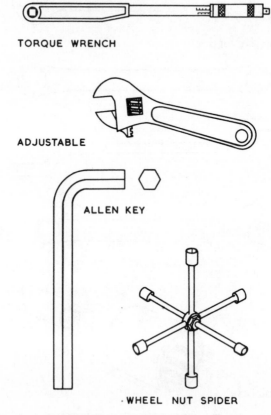

TORQUE WRENCH

ADJUSTABLE

ALLEN KEY

·WHEEL NUT SPIDER

Fig. 4.16 Special purpose wrenches and keys

**Combination wrenches.** The open end of the combination wrench is usually quicker to use because the ring key has to be lifted from the nut each time more leverage is required. The open-ended wrench is, however, liable to spring and slip when dealing with a very tight nut. Combined wrenches have the advantages of both types, an open end for quick movement and a closed or ring end for final tightening or releasing a stubborn nut. Both ends are the same nut size.

**Socket wrenches.** These are short rigid tubes which have an internal bi-hexagon recess at one end. The other end is solid and is pierced by a 13 mm or 19 mm square hole. A variety of handles is supplied which includes a brace or speed wrench, a large hinged handle, an off-set sliding handle and a ratchet handle. A series of extension bars and a universal joint are also included. Useful additions to the kit are sockets to fit square and hexagonal holes and projections such as those used in sump plugs and similar fittings. Screwdriver bits and sparking plug sockets are also very useful additions. Although these tools are expensive they do make the work of the mechanic both easier and quicker.

**Torque wrenches.** As all the important nuts and bolts on the vehicle must be tightened down to the correct torque loading, a torque wrench must always be available although it may not be a part of every mechanic's tool kit. These wrenches are usually used in conjunction with socket sets and consist of a long handle and some device for registering the opposition of the nut or bolt to being turned. This device may be (a) a spring-loaded break lever in which the tension of a spring is set to the correct loading and the lever 'breaks' or snaps sideways to warn when the nut is under the pre-set loading, (b) a calibrated dial gauge which measures the deflection of an arm which is a part of the handle, and (c) a long arm attached to the socket drive plug and moving over a calibrated torque scale at the handle end of the wrench, thus magnifying the deflection of the socket plug.

**Adjustable wrenches.** These have one fixed and one sliding jaw. The sliding jaw may be at right angles to the centre line of the wrench, or may be slightly inclined. While these wrenches are not suitable for general use on vehicles, because of the width and thickness of their jaws and because the sliding jaw is never really rigid, they can occasionally be of value.

**Allen keys** are small, L-shaped, hexagonal-sectioned bars which fit into hexagonal recesses in the heads of Allen and other special screws. These screws are not used very often on vehicles but are common on machine tools, being used where a recessed or sunken screw or bolt is essential, e.g. to hold the cutters of line boring and cylinder boring machines.

*Precautions*
(1) Whenever possible exert a steady pull on the wrench. If it must be pushed, always use the palm of the hand and keep the fingers out of the way. Always be ready for a wrench to slip or a nut to give suddenly.
(2) Make sure the wrench is of the correct size and is a good fit. Otherwise it may spring or break, or damage the nut.
(3) Never use anything on a wrench to increase its leverage.
(4) Never hammer a wrench unless it is designed to be used in this way.
(5) Always double check the torque loading of such bolts as those securing the engine bearings and cylinder heads.
(6) Always use an adjustable wrench in such a way that the movement of the wrench and nut forces the fixed jaw to take most of the load.

*Wrench sizes*
Wrenches are intended to be a good fit upon the hexagonal heads of bolts and nuts. These hexagons vary in size with the diameter of the bolt and with the form of screw thread, so wrenches are marked to indicate both the thread and the bolt size, e.g. $\frac{1}{4}$-in. BSW wrench or spanner sizes are classified as British, meaning BSW and BSF; American, meaning A/F and Unified; and Metric, meaning mm sizes. There are also the BA sizes.

As the hexagonal heads of the BSW threaded bolts have the same dimensions as the next larger size of BSF bolts the wrenches are often marked with both sizes, e.g. $\frac{1}{4}$-in. BSW, $\frac{5}{16}$-in. BSF. Note that the sizes marked on British wrenches refer to the diameter of the bolt and *not* the distance across the flat of the bolt head, i.e. the width of the wrench jaw. The American and Metric sizes *are* the measurements across the flats and between the wrench jaws.

The available sizes of the various wrenches are given in Tables 4.1, 4.2 and 4.3. These may usually be obtained in sets of seven.

*Metric sizes (mm)*

Table 4.1

| Open-ended | Ring keys | Combination | Sockets | |
|---|---|---|---|---|
| | | | $\frac{1}{2}$ *in* | $\frac{3}{4}$ *in* |
| 6 × 7 | 8 × 9 | Not normally available | From 10 mm to 28 mm in steps of 1 mm, then 30 mm and 32 mm | |
| 8 × 9 | 10 × 11 | | | |
| 10 × 11 | 12 × 13 | | | |
| 12 × 13 | 14 × 15 | | | |
| 14 × 15 | 16 × 17 | | | |
| 16 × 17 | 18 × 19 | | | |
| 18 × 19 | 20 × 22 | | | |
| 20 × 22 | 24 × 26 | | | |
| 21 × 23 | 28 × 30 | | | |
| 24 × 26 | — | | | |
| 25 × 28 | — | | | |
| 27 × 29 | — | | | |
| 28 × 30 | — | | | |
| 32 × 36 | — | | | |

*British (BSW and BSF)*

Table 4.2 (sizes in inches)

| Open-ended | Ring keys | Combination (same sized ends) | Sockets $\frac{1}{2}$ in | $\frac{3}{4}$ in |
|---|---|---|---|---|
| $\frac{1}{8} \times \frac{3}{16}$ | $\frac{1}{8} \times \frac{3}{16}$ | $\frac{1}{8}$ | $\frac{1}{8}$ | |
| $\frac{3}{16} \times \frac{1}{4}$ | $\frac{3}{16} \times \frac{1}{4}$ | $\frac{3}{16}$ | $\frac{3}{16}$ | |
| $\frac{1}{4} \times \frac{5}{16}$ | $\frac{1}{4} \times \frac{5}{16}$ | $\frac{1}{4}$ | $\frac{1}{4}$ | |
| $\frac{5}{16} \times \frac{3}{8}$ | $\frac{5}{16} \times \frac{3}{8}$ | $\frac{5}{16}$ | $\frac{5}{16}$ | |
| $\frac{3}{8} \times \frac{7}{16}$ | $\frac{3}{8} \times \frac{7}{16}$ | $\frac{3}{8}$ | $\frac{3}{8}$ | |
| $\frac{7}{16} \times \frac{1}{2}$ | $\frac{7}{16} \times \frac{1}{2}$ | $\frac{7}{16}$ | $\frac{7}{16}$ | |
| $\frac{1}{2} \times \frac{9}{16}$ | $\frac{1}{2} \times \frac{9}{16}$ | — | $\frac{1}{2}$ | |
| $\frac{9}{16} \times \frac{5}{8}$ | $\frac{9}{16} \times \frac{5}{8}$ | — | $\frac{9}{16}$ | |
| $\frac{9}{16} \times \frac{11}{16}$ | $\frac{9}{16} \times \frac{11}{16}$ | — | $\frac{5}{8}$ | |
| $\frac{5}{8} \times \frac{11}{16}$ | $\frac{5}{8} \times \frac{11}{16}$ | — | $\frac{11}{16}$ | |
| $\frac{5}{8} \times \frac{3}{4}$ | $\frac{5}{8} \times \frac{3}{4}$ | — | $\frac{3}{4}$ | |
| $\frac{11}{16} \times \frac{3}{4}$ | $\frac{11}{16} \times \frac{3}{4}$ | — | — | |
| $\frac{11}{16} \times \frac{13}{16}$ | $\frac{11}{16} \times \frac{13}{16}$ | — | — | |
| $\frac{3}{4} \times \frac{7}{8}$ | $\frac{3}{4} \times \frac{7}{8}$ | — | — | |
| $\frac{7}{8} \times 1$ | — | — | — | |
| $1 \times 1\frac{1}{8}$ | — | — | — | |

*BA sizes*

Wrenches from 0 to 11 BA are available in open-ended, ring and socket forms.

*American sizes (A/F and unified)*

Table 4.3

| Open-ended | Ring keys | Combination (same sized ends) | Sockets | |
|---|---|---|---|---|
| | | | $\frac{1}{2}$ in | $\frac{3}{4}$ in |
| $\frac{3}{16} \times \frac{1}{4}$ | — | $\frac{3}{8}$ | $\frac{3}{8}$ | |
| $\frac{1}{4} \times \frac{5}{16}$ | — | $\frac{7}{16}$ | $\frac{7}{16}$ | |
| $\frac{5}{16} \times \frac{3}{8}$ | $\frac{5}{16} \times \frac{3}{8}$ | $\frac{1}{2}$ | $\frac{1}{2}$ | |
| $\frac{3}{8} \times \frac{7}{16}$ | $\frac{3}{8} \times \frac{7}{16}$ | $\frac{9}{16}$ | $\frac{9}{16}$ | |
| $\frac{7}{16} \times \frac{1}{2}$ | $\frac{7}{16} \times \frac{1}{2}$ | $\frac{5}{8}$ | $\frac{19}{32}$ | |
| $\frac{1}{2} \times \frac{9}{16}$ | $\frac{1}{2} \times \frac{9}{16}$ | $\frac{3}{4}$ | $\frac{5}{8}$ | |
| $\frac{9}{16} \times \frac{5}{8}$ | $\frac{9}{16} \times \frac{5}{8}$ | — | $\frac{11}{16}$ | |
| $\frac{9}{16} \times \frac{11}{16}$ | — | — | $\frac{3}{4}$ | |
| $\frac{19}{32} \times \frac{11}{16}$ | $\frac{19}{32} \times \frac{11}{16}$ | — | $\frac{25}{32}$ | |
| $\frac{5}{8} \times \frac{11}{16}$ | $\frac{5}{8} \times \frac{11}{16}$ | — | $\frac{13}{16}$ | |
| $\frac{5}{8} \times \frac{3}{4}$ | $\frac{5}{8} \times \frac{3}{4}$ | — | $\frac{7}{8}$ | |
| $\frac{11}{16} \times \frac{3}{4}$ | — | — | $\frac{15}{16}$ | |
| $\frac{11}{16} \times \frac{13}{16}$ | $\frac{11}{16} \times \frac{13}{16}$ | — | $1$ | |
| $\frac{3}{4} \times \frac{7}{8}$ | $\frac{3}{4} \times \frac{7}{8}$ | — | $1\frac{1}{16}$ | |
| $\frac{25}{32} \times \frac{13}{16}$ | $\frac{25}{32} \times \frac{13}{16}$ | — | $1\frac{1}{8}$ | |
| $\frac{13}{16} \times \frac{7}{8}$ | $\frac{13}{16} \times \frac{7}{8}$ | — | $1\frac{3}{16}$ | |
| $\frac{7}{8} \times 1$ | — | — | $1\frac{1}{4}$ | |
| $\frac{15}{16} \times 1$ | $\frac{15}{16} \times 1$ | — | — | |

# 5    Metal-cutting Tools

## Cutting action

When brittle metals such as cast iron are cut a series of small chips is produced, Fig. 5.1(a). As the tool moves over the work a layer of metal ahead of the tool is first compressed by it and is then sheared, and finally breaks away in small pieces.

When ductile metals such as mild steel are cut a continuous chip is usually produced, Fig. 5.1(b). As the tool moves over the work the metal ahead of it is forced to flow over the face of the tool. This is due to the pressure exerted by the tool, but the chip is not sheared. Continuous chips can be a source of danger to the machine operator so some cutting tools may have a ground step on the tool face which acts as a chip breaker.

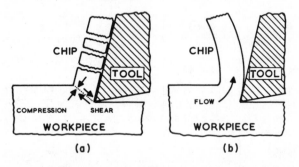

Fig. 5.1 Cutting action: (a) brittle material; (b) ductile material

## Cutting angles

The tools used to cut metals must be harder and tougher than the metals being cut. The angles which form the cutting edge must be nearer to a right angle than those of tools used for cutting softer materials, e.g. a wood-cutting chisel may be ground to 30°, while a steel-cutting chisel would be about 60°. These angles are very important, and equally important are those which prevent the tool rubbing against the work. These angles are called cutting, rake and clearance angles.

**Rake.** The angle between the side of the cutting edge and the perpendicular from the metal surface at the tool-cutting edge is called the *rake angle* and it is this angle which does the work of tearing off the metal parallel to, and in front of, the cutting edge. Rake angles will therefore be different for tools used to cut the different metals, a soft and ductile metal needing a tool with a larger rake angle than for a harder and tougher metal.

**Clearance.** The angle between the other side of the cutting edge and the surface cut by the edge is called the *clearance angle*. This angle is made so that only the cutting edge is in contact with the cut surface; no other part of the tool can rub and so lift the cutting edge from the surface.

Where a tool is fed into the metal at an angle laterally, as well as along the centre line of the tool, as in machine work of many kinds, the tool has to be given rake and clearance angles to suit this feed, i.e. it must be given side rake and clearance in addition to top rake and clearance. Extra clearance may also be needed in some circumstances, for example in boring operations where the bore diameter is small in relation to the tool size.

### Common tool angles

**Chisels.** The cutting edge of a cold chisel should be ground to an angle of about 60° for most garage work. An angle of 30° is more suitable for aluminium and similar soft metals, the angle being increased as the metal worked is harder – up to 60° for iron and steel.

The angle at which the chisel is inclined to the surface of the metal will alter the rake and clearance angles, see Fig. 5.2(a). To give a clearance angle of 10° the chisel must be inclined at about 40°. If the cutting angle is 30° then the chisel should be inclined at about 25° to give the correct 10° clearance angle.

**Lathe and boring tools.** The rake angles required for machine work such as boring and turning with high-speed steel tools are usually:

(a) For cutting hard steels, irons, and bronzes: 8°.

(b) For cutting softer types of the above metals: 14°.

(c) For cutting mild steel: 14° to 18°.

(d) For cutting aluminium and similar soft metals: 30°.

The clearance angles are usually between 6° and 8° but should permit no more than just adequate clearance of the cutting edge in any situation, see Fig. 5.2(b).

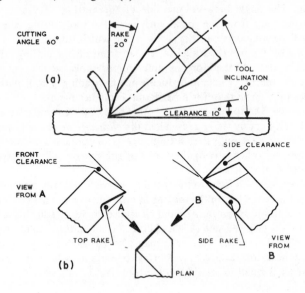

Fig. 5.2 Rake and clearance: (a) chisel; (b) lathe tool

**Drills.** No tool can cut without a clearance for the cutting edge. On the standard twist drill, Fig. 5.3(a), this angle is 12° and it can be seen by looking along a cutting edge (or lip). The rake angle is determined by the helix angle of the flutes and is usually $27\frac{1}{2}°$. The two cutting edges must be equal in length and be at 59° to the drill centre line. They must also be parallel to each other when viewed from the end of the drill. The flutes are used to allow the cuttings to escape and the lands are ground away, apart from a narrow edge to provide a clearance for the body through the hole already cut by the cutting edges. The cutting angles may be larger for softer metals, e.g. 90° for drilling copper and aluminium, Fig. 5.3(b).
*Note.* The drill is discussed in detail on p. 75 and the method of sharpening the drill is dealt with on p. 73.

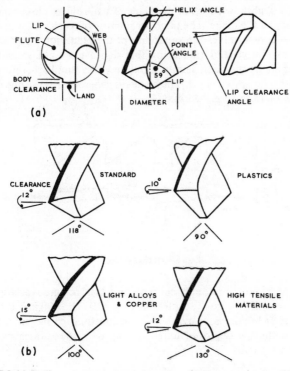

Fig. 5.3 (a) Drill cutting and clearance angles. (b) Point angles for different materials

**Scrapers.** Flat scrapers (Fig. 4.3) are ground to have a slight curve on their end face which must have very sharp edges. The end face only must be ground, never the side faces, so the cutting angle is 90°. Curved scrapers (Fig. 4.4) must be hollow ground, the sides being ground to form two very sharp and curved cutting edges.

**Punches.** The point of the centre punch should be ground to an angle of 60°, while the marker punch, used to define scribed lines, should have a 90° point.

**Hacksaws.** The teeth of a hacksaw blade (Fig. 5.4) have only a very small rake angle and clearance angle to provide a stronger cutting edge. The cutting edges are slightly offset alternately so the cut made is slightly wider than the blade. This provides clearance for the body of the blade. The pitch, or number of teeth per 25 mm of the blade, determines the suitability of the blade for a particular purpose, the general rule being that at least 3 teeth should be cutting at any moment. Thin sections and tube should therefore be cut with a fine-pitch blade. The blade for general use is the one with a pitch of 18 teeth per 25 mm.

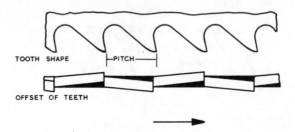

TOOTH SHAPE |—PITCH—|

OFFSET OF TEETH

Fig. 5.4 Hacksaw teeth

**Files.** Most files are double-cut types in which 60° grooves are cut at 45° and then 70° to the centre line (Fig. 5.5). The file surface then consists of hundreds of pyramid-shaped teeth, each having a side rake as the file is moved longitudinally over the surface of the metal being cut.

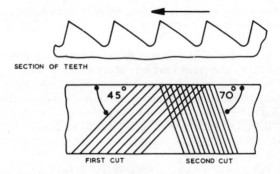

SECTION OF TEETH

45° 70°

FIRST CUT          SECOND CUT

Fig. 5.5 File teeth

## Tool sharpening

**Chisels.** Chisels are ground to their correct angles on a grinding wheel which may be bench or pillar mounted and which is driven at a high speed by an electric motor. Except where the wheel and the machine are designed for side grinding, only the periphery of the wheel should be used. A number of light cuts should be taken in preference to one or two heavy cuts. The faces forming the cutting angle should be checked against a setting gauge or a protractor. A rough or medium-rough wheel should be used and care must always be taken to avoid overheating the cutting edge.

**Punches.** Centre, marking and pin punches are reground in a similar manner but are rotated smoothly while in contact with the wheel. Pin punches should not be ground on their cylindrical sides. Always feed the punch end-on into the periphery of the wheel, and rotate it slowly.

**Scrapers.** These must be sharpened only on an oil stone. The end only of the flat scraper is rubbed on the stone, rocking it slightly from side to side as it is moved up and down the stone until a fine sharp unbroken edge is produced. Curved scrapers are hollow ground and this part may be sharpened using a half round or round stone. The side faces may then be carefully ground on the flat oil stone to obtain the very sharp edge required.

**Drills.** When a drill requires sharpening it is most important that the cutting and clearance angles be ground correctly. It is impossible to produce an accurately-sized hole with a drill which has been ground to an eye judgement. Such a drill might cut for a time but the hole will be much larger than the size of the drill. This is because the cutting edges will not be of the same length and the longer edge will produce an outsized diameter (Fig. 5.6). If the angles of the cutting edges are not quite the same one edge will do all the work and will be dulled before the other. Too great a clearance weakens the cutting edge and it will overheat or dull very quickly. Overheating destroys the temper of the drill and so softens the cutting edges. Too small a clearance angle results in the rubbing of the cutting edges and prevents the drill feeding into the material.

Twist drills should be sharpened with the aid of a drill grinding attachment. This is a vee-shaped channel which is fitted to the bench grinder and set at the required angle to the grinding wheel. The drill is clamped into the channel and fed into the wheel by a thumb screw, the channel being pivoted by hand.

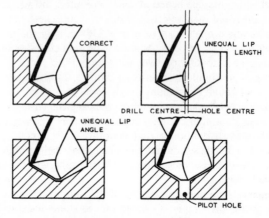

Fig. 5.6 Point faults in twist drills

Drills are designed to cut at certain speeds, the larger the drill the lower the speed. A correctly-ground drill will be overheated and its temper destroyed if it is used at excessive speeds.

Excessive pressure on a drill should also be avoided. If the drill does not break or bend the cutting edges will be splintered. In most work the drill will feed itself through the material with only a steady pressure being required.

*Grinding precautions*

(1) Check the wheel for security and truth.

(2) Check that the tool rest is secure and close to the wheel.

(3) Wear goggles.

(4) Keep the hands and clothing away from the wheel.

(5) Avoid inhaling the stone dust.

(6) Sharpen the wheel with a diamond stone dresser if the cutting face has worn ridged or if it is not at 90° to the sides of the wheel.

(7) Do not use the wheel for soft metals as this clogs the face.

(8) Do not use the side of the wheel. This may cause it to burst.

(9) Use the whole cutting face of the wheel and not one part.

(10) Hold the tool firmly to avoid chatter and the possibility of it being thrown from the wheel.

(11) Avoid excessive pressures on the grinding wheel.

(12) Do not overheat the tool.

(13) Do not quench tools to cool them. This causes cracks in the . cutting edges. In any case an overheated tool will never again function as was originally intended.

## The drill

The drill is an accurately-finished, hardened and tempered tool. It is used to produce an accurately-sized hole in material. Drilling is the operation of producing a hole and it should not be confused with boring. Boring is the operation in which the size of an existing hole is increased, brought to an accurate size, and made round and parallel.

The most common type of drill is the twist drill, Fig. 5.7(a). The body of the drill is an accurately-ground and cylindrical piece of carbon or alloy steel. Carbon steel drills are usually blue in colour and are suitable for most general work. Alloy steel drills are bright and are sometimes called high speed, or H.S., drills because they can take larger cuts at higher speeds. Two spiral or helical flutes are machined from the body of the drill at an angle of $27\frac{1}{2}°$ to its axis. These flutes are used to help provide the correct cutting angle, to provide an escape path for the cuttings, and to allow lubricant to reach the cutting edges. The portions of metal left between the flutes are called *lands* and the accuracy of their diameter determines the size of the drill. The lower portions of the lands are reduced in diameter to leave only a narrow land upper edge, so reducing friction.

The tip of the drill is accurately ground to a cutting angle which varies with the different materials to be drilled. The standard angle is 59° and this is suitable for most work. A cutting angle of between 45° and 50° should be used on cast iron. The angle for brass is 45° also, but a drill designed for brass work has straight flutes. Soft metals such as copper and aluminium are best drilled by a 90° angle, being ground to leave a small central point to act as a guide. Very tough metals like manganese steel are best drilled by a special drill having an angle of twist of about 24° and a cutting angle of about 75°. When drilling sheet metal the cutting angle should be greater, i.e. more obtuse. This prevents the point of the drill breaking through before the drill has cut to the full diameter.

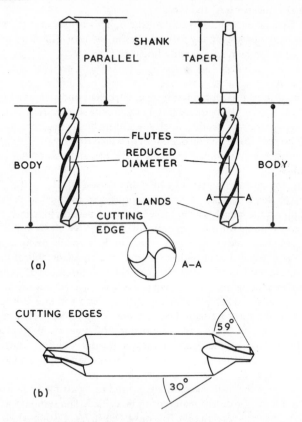

Fig. 5.7 (a) Twist drill. (b) Countersink or centre drill

The shank of the drill may be parallel or tapered. Usually drills larger in diameter than 13 mm have taper shanks. These fit directly into the spindle of the drilling machine, replacing the taper-shanked chuck used for the parallel shank and smaller drills.

*Countersink drills*

A combined pilot drill and countersink is used where countersunk-head machine screws are to be employed. They are also used for centring work which is to be turned in a lathe. The countersink drill, Fig. 5.7(b), has a parallel centre body, the diameter of which gives the drill its size. Both ends of the body are finished by a short pilot drill and a 60° angled cutting edge. Pilot hole drilling and countersinking are thus completed in one operation. The drill portions must be ground with the same care as the standard drill. The weakest point is the intersection of the drill and the countersink, and the drill must be used carefully to avoid breakage. There must be no vibration between the work and the drill, and excessive speeds and pressures must be avoided. The feed must be started slowly.

*Drill sizes*

Drills are manufactured in a very wide range of sizes. Apart from the commonly used fraction sizes there are metric sizes. Under 13 mm diameter there are intermediate sizes coded by numbers and letters. All these sizes are integrated in tables which assist in the selection of a drill to produce a non-standard hole, e.g. if a hole of 7·40 mm diameter were required, then this size drill would be chosen. If the hole were to be slightly smaller, then a $\frac{9}{32}$ in. diameter drill could be used.

*Drill gauges*

These are metal plates pierced by drilled holes, the hole sizes being stamped alongside the holes. Gauges are available for fraction, metric, number and letter drills. Tapping drill sizes are also available for the various thread forms.

*Cutting lubricants*

These are used to both cool and lubricate the cutting edges of the drill, so prolonging the life of the drill and helping to produce a hole free from heat distortion. Cast iron, brass and bakelite are drilled without a lubricant but care must be taken to avoid overheating. In deep drilling of these materials the drill may be cooled by a jet of compressed air. A soluble oil (mixed with water) or a sulphurized oil should be used for drilling mild steel. Soluble oil should also be used when drilling phosphor-bronze, copper, and aluminium. Aluminium and its alloys can also be lubricated by paraffin.

*Drilling machines,* Fig. 5.8

Drilling machines are used to hold and rotate the drill. They may be hand operated or powered by compressed air or electricity. Powered machines have the advantages of leaving both hands free to direct the drill and are faster in operation. Hand-powered drilling machines are light in weight and can be used to drill holes of up to 7 mm diameter in soft or thin materials in almost any situation. The breast drill is larger and heavier and can accommodate drills of up to 13 mm in diameter. Both have taper wedge action chucks driven through reduction bevel gearing, the breast drilling usually having two alternative ratios.

Compressed-air machines drive their chucks by a small turbine motor, acting through reduction gears. These machines are very light and compact, and are most useful in confined spaces. Their disadvantage is the length of supply hose required, which is even more vulnerable to damage than an electric cable.

Electrically-powered machines consist of an electric motor which drives the chuck through reduction gearing. Fixed machines for larger operations and portable machines are in general use. The portable machines vary in size and drill capacity, the more common small ones accommodating drills up to 6 mm or 8 mm diameter. There are also two-speed portable machines which can use larger drills.

The fixed drilling machines may be either bench mounted or pillar types. Both have a heavy, rigid base and a vertical pillar. The motor, gearing, and driving spindle and chuck are mounted on the pillar and can be swung from side to side as well as raised and lowered. The floor-mounted pillar drill has a separate work-table which can be moved in a similar manner to the drilling assembly.

The bench drill will usually accommodate drills of up to 13 mm diameter. The pillar drill will accommodate similar drills and also take taper shank drills, according to its size and power, of up to 75 mm diameter.

Chucks with taper shanks are fitted into the driving spindle of the machine. Morse taper adaptor sleeves are available to convert

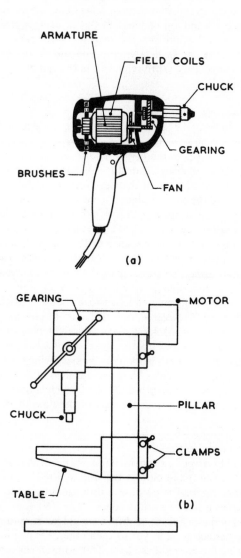

Fig. 5.8 Drilling machines: (a) portable drill; (b) pillar drill

the drill tapers to suit the machine taper. The sleeves are fitted by pressing them firmly on to the drill shank, using a piece of wood between the drill point and the machine work table to prevent damage. Sleeves and drills are removed from the machine spindle by a steel wedge driven through a slot in the spindle above the tail of the taper.

## Holding the work for drilling

Work which is to be drilled must always be securely clamped, unless it is too large or too heavy to move during the operation. The greatest danger to the person and to the quality of the work lies in the moment when the drill breaks through the underside of the material. At this instant the steady force on the drill point is unopposed and the cutting edges bite into the material. If the work is loose it will spin around and cause damage, possibly injuring the operator and ruining the work. This danger is always present and especial care should be taken when drilling sheet metal and using the larger types of portable electric drilling machines. The force on the drill must always be eased off as the hole nears completion.

Drill vices are available which will securely hold most small work, the vice itself being clamped to the slotted machine table. Another method for larger work is to clamp it to the machine table by clamp plates and packing pieces, the tightening of the clamp bolts trapping the work to the table. Cylindrical work is best secured in channels, both work and channels being clamped to the machine table. When holes have to be drilled at awkward angles the work may be clamped to a tilt plate which is then clamped to the machine table such that the axis of the hole to be drilled is vertical.

## Marking out for drilling

A hole should never be drilled without its position being properly marked, and the initial cuts of the drill assisted by a fairly deep centre punch mark. The point of a drill cannot start to cut into a flat surface as it has no cutting edges.

The location of a hole to be drilled should be marked out by two firm, thin, scribed lines at 90° to each other, their point of intersection being the centre of the hole. This point is then carefully and lightly marked by a centre punch. A circle of the hole diameter is then scribed and about eight light punches marked upon it at equal intervals. The centre is then punched deeper to help the drill to start.

Drilling is then commenced, but before the drill is cutting to the full diameter the depression made is checked for being central in the marked circle. If it is then the drilling of the hole is carried on to completion. If it is not then the drilled hole must be corrected by 'drawing' the point from its existing centre to the correct centre. This is done by cutting a groove with a half round chisel, or a diamond point chisel, or even a centre punch. The groove must be cut across the widest part of the uncut metal inside the circle from the edge of the circle to the drilled centre. The drill point is then drawn along the groove to the correct centre and a little more cutting carried out. This is a trial and error process until the depression cut is found to be centralized in the circle. When this is so the drilling operation is continued and the hole completed.

*Drilling faults*

The following table gives common faults which occur during drilling operations togehter with their possible causes.

Table 5.1

| *Fault* | *Possible causes* |
| --- | --- |
| Oversized hole produced | 1. Cutting edges are of unequal length<br>2. Cutting angles are unequal<br>3. Machine spindle loose or bent<br>4. Chuck loose |
| Drill corners being broken off | 1. Wrong lubricant<br>2. Lubricant not reaching the cutting edges<br>3. Cutting speed too high<br>4. Hard spots in the material |
| Drill broken | 1. Dulled cutting edges<br>2. Clearance angle too small<br>3. Pressure on drill too high<br>4. Work or drill insecurely held<br>5. Flutes choked by cuttings |
| Rough hole produced | 1. Dulled cutting edges<br>2. Point incorrectly ground<br>3. Lubricant lacking or incorrect |

## Drilling precautions

Care must always be taken when using tools, but electric drilling machines can be particularly dangerous if the operator is careless. The following precautions should always be taken before and during drilling operations.

### For personal safety

(1) Check that electrical cables are sound. There must be no loose or bare wires and the machines must be properly earthed.

(2) Use the shortest possible length of cable to reach the work properly. See that it is not likely to be run over or become soaked in oil or water. See that it is not likely to cause someone to trip over it or be damaged by the movement of another car.

(3) Check that the work is securely clamped or is too big to move when the drill breaks through.

(4) Check that the drill is firmly held by the chuck. Wipe oil from the hands and hold the machine firmly – be ready for it being twisted out of the hands on break-through.

### For good work

(1) Check that the drill is correctly sharpened.

(2) Check that the drill is secure in the chuck and the chuck secure in the machine.

(3) Check that the work is properly clamped.

(4) When large holes are to be drilled, drill a smaller pilot hole first to ensure accuracy and a better finish.

(5) Select the correct speed for the size of drill.

(6) Exert a steady force on the drill – let the drill feed itself through the hole.

(7) Check the drill for correct location – 'draw' if necessary.

(8) Use the correct lubricant. Clear the cuttings at intervals.

(9) Be ready for the drill breaking through.

(10) Do not allow the drill to cut into the machine plate or other clamping devices.

**Screw Threads**

Screw threads are made in distinct forms or shapes to suit different purposes. Individual countries have adopted varying forms to suit the same purposes. The most widely used thread form is that of the vee, and vee threads of various angles are used wherever a secure but temporary joint is needed. Because the faces of the thread are at an angle to the tightening force a great deal of friction is produced and to a fair extent these thread forms resist being slackened by vibration and shock.

Other forms of thread are as follows (see Fig. 6.1):

(a) *Buttress thread.* This has one face at 90° to the thread axis and the other at 45°, and will transmit motion in one direction only. This shape permits the easy meshing and release of a half-nut engagement device and is used in the quick release bench vice.

(b) *Square thread.* When loaded this thread has much less friction than the vee thread so it is suited to the transmission of motion in either direction. It is used in the plain bench vice and other clamping devices.

(c) *Knuckle thread.* This will transmit motion in either direction and also has less friction than the vee thread.

(d) *Acme thread.* This also can transmit motion in either direction and has less friction than the vee thread. Because of their shapes both the knuckle thread and the Acme thread permit the easy meshing of a nut or half-nut engagement device. Both are used for lathe and boring bar lead screws.

**Thread gauges**

The motor mechanic's first interest in screw threads is that of being able to recognize them in order to choose the correct sizes of spanner, die-nut, or taps and dies. He must also know the most suitable thread to use in a given situation; for example, a coarse thread when tapping aluminium alloy as this is less likely to be torn out when the bolt or stud is tightened.

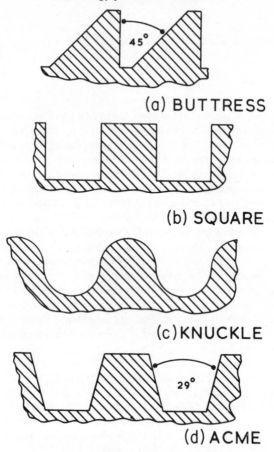

Fig. 6.1 Forms of screw thread

Thread gauges (Fig. 6.2) are available which ease greatly the job of identifying unfamiliar thread forms. A very common type of gauge comprises a set of thin steel plates arranged after the style of a set of feeler gauges. Every plate in each set is cut to the same thread form but a different pitch. The plates are meshed in turn with the unknown thread until one is found which fits correctly.

The thread size is then read on the plate. Sets are made for each thread form; e.g. a Whitworth set makes possible the identification of BSW, BSF, and BSP threads. Once the thread form and pitch are known the correct die-nuts, or taps and dies, can be selected. Tables are then used to determine the correct sizes of drill to use to allow the size of bolt to pass through (clearance size) or the size to drill to form an internal thread by means of a tap (tapping size). Simplified forms of these tables are given with the descriptions of the various vee threads.

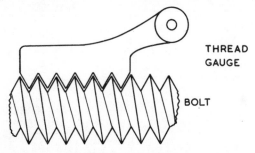

Fig. 6.2 Screw thread gauge

**Terms used in describing vee threads**

*Outside diameter* or major diameter. This is the distance across the thread, measured at 90° to the thread axis.

*The crest*, top or point of the thread is its outermost part.

*The root* of the thread is its innermost part.

*The core diameter or minor diameter* is the distance between the roots of the thread, measured at 90° to the thread axis.

*The depth* of the thread is the distance between the crests and the roots, measured at 90° to the thread axis.

*The pitch* of the thread is the distance between a point on one thread and a similar one on the next, measured parallel to the thread axis. It is also the distance moved by the nut in one complete revolution of a single-start thread.

These are the main features of the vee thread. Other terms are illustrated in Fig. 6.3.

When a nut has to move further in one revolution than it would go with a single thread then two or more threads are used, each pitch, or lead, being two or three times that of the single thread.

These are termed multiple-start threads and are often used in starter motor driving gear arrangements. The thread forms are square and two threads are cut side by side.

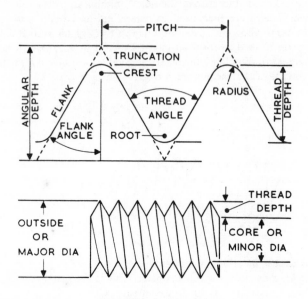

Fig. 6.3 Screw thread terms

### Standard vee threads

The British vee threads are the British Standard Whitworth (BSW); the British Standard Fine (BSF); the British Standard Pipe (BSP or Gas); and the British Association (BA).

### BS Whitworth thread

This is the thread form used for most general engineering purposes, and may be used where studs or bolts are to be screwed into soft metals (Fig. 6.4). It is a strong thread form and is coarse in pitch, i.e. has a small number of crests or threads per inch of length, see Fig. 6.5(a). It is not suitable for situations in which much vibration or shock occur. The angle between the thread faces, thread angle, is 55° and the crests and roots are both rounded. The depth of the thread is 0·64 of the pitch.

The sizes of drills required for the tapping and clearance of Whitworth threads are given in Tables 6.1 to 6.7 in alternative drill size systems, e.g. a $\frac{1}{2}$ in. Whitworth bolt will have 12 threads per inch and the tapping size drill can be $\frac{25}{64}$ in. 9·9 mm, or X in the letter drill system.

A blank space in a column means there is no equivalent in that system, e.g. there are no equivalent sizes of drill in the number or letter systems beyond $\frac{1}{2}$ in. Whitworth. Size is thread diameter or number. T.P.I. is the abbreviation for threads per inch.

Table 6.1 Whitworth (BSW)

| Size inch | T.P.I. | Tapping sizes | | | Clearance sizes | | |
|---|---|---|---|---|---|---|---|
| | | *Inches* | mm | *Number or letter* | *Inches* | mm | *Number or letter* |
| $\frac{3}{16}$ | 24 | $\frac{9}{64}$ | 3·6 | 27 | $\frac{13}{64}$ | 5·1 | 7 |
| $\frac{1}{4}$ | 20 | $\frac{3}{16}$ | 4·7 | 12 | $\frac{17}{64}$ | 6·7 | H |
| $\frac{5}{16}$ | 18 | $\frac{1}{4}$ | 6·4 | E | $\frac{21}{64}$ | 8·3 | Q |
| $\frac{3}{8}$ | 16 | $\frac{19}{64}$ | 7·5 | N | $\frac{25}{64}$ | 9·9 | X |
| $\frac{7}{16}$ | 14 | $\frac{23}{64}$ | 9·1 | U | $\frac{29}{64}$ | 11·5 | — |
| $\frac{1}{2}$ | 12 | $\frac{25}{64}$ | 9·9 | X | $\frac{33}{64}$ | 13 | — |
| $\frac{9}{16}$ | 12 | $\frac{29}{64}$ | 11·5 | — | $\frac{37}{64}$ | 14·7 | — |
| $\frac{5}{8}$ | 11 | $\frac{1}{2}$ | 12·7 | — | $\frac{41}{64}$ | 16·3 | — |
| $\frac{11}{16}$ | 11 | $\frac{37}{64}$ | 14·7 | — | $\frac{45}{64}$ | 17·9 | — |
| $\frac{3}{4}$ | 10 | $\frac{5}{8}$ | 15·9 | — | $\frac{49}{64}$ | 19·4 | — |

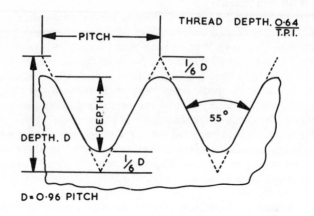

Fig. 6.4 Whitworth thread form

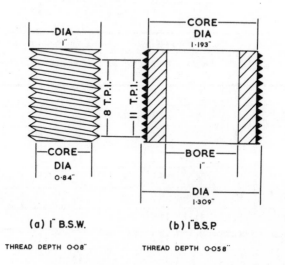

Fig. 6.5 Whitworth threads

## British Standard Fine (BSF) thread

This thread is used in situations where shock and vibration are common. It has the same thread form as the Whitworth but has more threads per inch, i.e. it is of a finer pitch. Both the BSW and BSF threads have been used in vehicle work for many years but are now being replaced by the Unified Thread.

Table 6.2 British Standard Fine (BSF)

| Size inch | T.P.I. | Tapping sizes | | | Clearance sizes | | |
|---|---|---|---|---|---|---|---|
| | | *Inches* | mm | *Number or letter* | *Inches* | mm | *Number or letter* |
| $\frac{7}{32}$ | 28 | $\frac{11}{64}$ | 4·4 | 17 | $\frac{15}{64}$ | 5·7 | 2 |
| $\frac{1}{4}$ | 26 | $\frac{13}{64}$ | 5·2 | 6 | $\frac{17}{64}$ | 6·7 | H |
| $\frac{9}{32}$ | 26 | $\frac{15}{64}$ | 5·9 | B | $\frac{19}{64}$ | 7·5 | N |
| $\frac{5}{16}$ | 22 | $\frac{1}{4}$ | 6·4 | E | $\frac{21}{64}$ | 8·3 | Q |
| $\frac{3}{8}$ | 20 | $\frac{5}{16}$ | 7·9 | O | $\frac{25}{64}$ | 9·9 | X |
| $\frac{7}{16}$ | 18 | $\frac{23}{64}$ | 9·1 | U | $\frac{29}{64}$ | 11·5 | — |
| $\frac{1}{2}$ | 16 | $\frac{27}{64}$ | 10·7 | — | $\frac{33}{64}$ | 13 | — |
| $\frac{9}{16}$ | 16 | $\frac{31}{64}$ | 12·3 | — | $\frac{37}{64}$ | 14·7 | — |
| $\frac{5}{8}$ | 14 | $\frac{17}{32}$ | 13·5 | — | $\frac{41}{64}$ | 16·3 | — |
| $\frac{11}{16}$ | 14 | $\frac{19}{32}$ | 15·1 | — | $\frac{45}{64}$ | 17·9 | — |
| $\frac{3}{4}$ | 12 | $\frac{41}{64}$ | 16·3 | — | $\frac{49}{64}$ | 19·4 | — |

## British Standard Pipe (Gas) or BSP thread

This thread has the same form as the BSW, but has a much finer pitch in relation to the diameter, see Fig. 6.5(b). This is to avoid cutting too deeply into the thin walls of pipes. It is important to remember that, unless otherwise specified, the pipe sizes refer to the bore of the pipe and *not* the outside diameter, e.g. the ½ in. gas thread on steel pipe has an outside diameter of 0·825 in. while its core diameter is 0·734 in. – both being well over the ½ in. or 0·5 in.

Table 6.3 British Standard Pipe (Gas) or BSP

| Size of bore and thread inch | T.P.I. | Tapping sizes | | | Clearance sizes | | |
|---|---|---|---|---|---|---|---|
| | | Inches | mm | Number or letter | Inches | mm | Number or letter |
| $\frac{1}{8}$ | 28 | $\frac{11}{32}$ | 8·7 | — | $\frac{25}{64}$ | 9·9 | — |
| $\frac{1}{4}$ | 19 | $\frac{15}{32}$ | 11·9 | — | $\frac{17}{32}$ | 13·5 | — |
| $\frac{3}{8}$ | 19 | $\frac{19}{32}$ | 15 | — | $\frac{43}{64}$ | 17·1 | — |
| $\frac{1}{2}$ | 14 | $\frac{3}{4}$ | 19 | — | $\frac{27}{32}$ | 21·4 | — |
| $\frac{5}{8}$ | 14 | $\frac{53}{64}$ | 21 | — | $\frac{59}{64}$ | 23·4 | — |
| $\frac{3}{4}$ | 14 | $\frac{31}{32}$ | 24·6 | — | $1\frac{3}{64}$ | 26·6 | — |
| $\frac{7}{8}$ | 14 | $1\frac{7}{64}$ | 28·2 | — | $1\frac{13}{64}$ | 30·5 | — |
| 1 | 11 | $1\frac{15}{64}$ | 30·5 | — | $1\frac{21}{64}$ | 33·7 | — |

## British Association (BA) thread

The BA thread form (Fig. 6.6) is used for threads under about ¼ in. particularly those associated with electrical work. The angle of the thread is 47½° degrees and the crests and roots are rounded. The depth is ⅗ of the pitch.

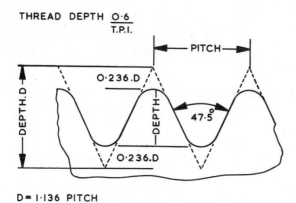

THREAD DEPTH $\dfrac{0.6}{\text{T.P.I.}}$

D = 1·136 PITCH

Fig. 6.6 BA thread form

Table 6.4 British Association (BA)

| Size | T.P.I. | Tapping sizes | | | Clearance sizes | | |
|------|--------|--------|------|-----------------|--------|------|-----------------|
|      |        | *Inches* | mm | *Number or letter* | *Inches* | mm | *Number or letter* |
| 0 | 25·4 | $\frac{13}{64}$ | 5·1 | 7 | $\frac{1}{4}$ | 6·3 | E |
| 1 | 28·2 | $\frac{11}{64}$ | 4·5 | 16 | $\frac{7}{32}$ | 5·5 | 3 |
| 2 | 31·4 | $\frac{5}{32}$ | 4 | 22 | — | 4·9 | 11 |
| 3 | 34·8 | $\frac{9}{64}$ | 3·5 | 29 | $\frac{11}{64}$ | 4·4 | 17 |
| 4 | 38·5 | $\frac{1}{8}$ | 3·3 | 30 | — | 3·7 | 26 |
| 5 | 43·1 | $\frac{7}{64}$ | 2·7 | 36 | — | 3·3 | 30 |
| 6 | 47·9 | $\frac{3}{32}$ | 2·4 | 42 | — | 2·9 | 32 |
| 7 | 52·9 | — | 2 | 45 | — | 2·6 | 38 |
| 8 | 59·2 | — | 1·9 | 49 | — | 2·4 | 42 |
| 9 | 64·9 | — | 1·6 | 52 | $\frac{5}{64}$ | 2 | 47 |
| 10 | 72·5 | — | 1·4 | 54 | — | 1·8 | 50 |

**American National Standard (Sellers) fine and coarse (ANF and ANC) threads**

The ANF and ANC threads (Fig. 6.7) are the American equivalents of the fine and coarse Whitworth threads. The thread angle is 60° and the crests and roots are flattened to $\frac{1}{8}$ of the depth of the thread.

Table 6.5 American National Fine (ANF)

| Size inch | T.P.I. | Tapping sizes | | | Clearance sizes | | |
|---|---|---|---|---|---|---|---|
| | | *Inches* | mm | *Number or letter* | *Inches* | mm | *Number or letter* |
| $\frac{1}{4}$ | 28 | $\frac{7}{32}$ | 5·5 | 3 | — | 6·5 | F |
| $\frac{5}{16}$ | 24 | — | 6·9 | I | — | 8·2 | P |
| $\frac{3}{8}$ | 24 | $\frac{21}{64}$ | 8·3 | Q | — | 9·8 | W |
| $\frac{7}{16}$ | 20 | $\frac{25}{64}$ | 9·9 | — | $\frac{29}{64}$ | 11·5 | — |
| $\frac{1}{2}$ | 20 | $\frac{29}{64}$ | 11·5 | — | $\frac{33}{64}$ | 13 | — |
| $\frac{9}{16}$ | 18 | $\frac{33}{64}$ | 13 | — | $\frac{37}{64}$ | 14·7 | — |
| $\frac{5}{8}$ | 18 | $\frac{37}{64}$ | 14·5 | — | $\frac{41}{64}$ | 16·3 | — |
| $\frac{3}{4}$ | 16 | $\frac{11}{16}$ | 17·5 | — | $\frac{49}{64}$ | 19·4 | — |
| $\frac{7}{8}$ | 14 | $\frac{13}{16}$ | 20·5 | — | $\frac{57}{64}$ | 22·6 | — |
| 1 | 14 | $\frac{59}{64}$ | 23·4 | — | $1\frac{1}{32}$ | 25·8 | — |

Table 6.6 American National Coarse (ANC)

| Size inch | T.P.I. | Tapping sizes | | | Clearance sizes | | |
|---|---|---|---|---|---|---|---|
| | | Inches | mm | Number or letter | Inches | mm | Number or letter |
| $\frac{1}{4}$ | 20 | $\frac{13}{64}$ | 5·1 | 7 | — | 6·5 | F |
| $\frac{5}{16}$ | 18 | $\frac{17}{64}$ | 6·7 | G | — | 8·2 | P |
| $\frac{3}{8}$ | 16 | $\frac{5}{16}$ | 7·9 | O | — | 9·8 | W |
| $\frac{7}{16}$ | 14 | — | 9·3 | U | $\frac{29}{64}$ | 11·5 | — |
| $\frac{1}{2}$ | 13 | $\frac{27}{64}$ | 10·7 | — | $\frac{33}{64}$ | 13 | — |
| $\frac{9}{16}$ | 12 | $\frac{31}{64}$ | 12·3 | — | $\frac{37}{64}$ | 14·7 | — |
| $\frac{5}{8}$ | 11 | $\frac{17}{32}$ | 13·5 | — | $\frac{41}{64}$ | 16·3 | — |
| $\frac{3}{4}$ | 10 | $\frac{41}{64}$ | 16·3 | — | $\frac{49}{64}$ | 19·4 | — |
| $\frac{7}{8}$ | 9 | $\frac{49}{64}$ | 19·4 | — | $\frac{57}{64}$ | 22·6 | — |
| 1 | 8 | $\frac{7}{8}$ | 22·2 | — | $1\frac{1}{32}$ | 25·8 | — |

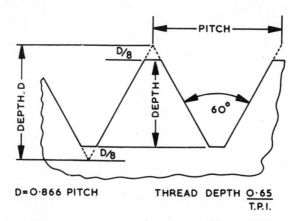

D=0·866 PITCH          THREAD DEPTH $\frac{0·65}{T.P.I.}$

Fig. 6.7 National standard (Sellers) thread, U.S.A.

**Metric or international thread**

Metric threads are used on the Continent and have a similar form to the American National thread. Most countries of the world are now using, or changing over to, a metric system of measurement. Britain must keep down her costs by also changing over to a metric system if she is to retain and increase her trade with these countries. In order to achieve this British Industry is adopting the metric system of measurement generally and, particularly, metric screw threads. The current international recognized threads are the ISO metric (BS 3643) and the ISO inch unified (BS 1580).

Table 6.7 Metric

| Size in mm | Pitch in mm | Tapping sizes | | | Clearance sizes | | |
|---|---|---|---|---|---|---|---|
| | | *Inches* | *mm* | *Number or letter* | *Inches* | *mm* | *Number or letter* |
| 6 | 1 | — | 5 | 9 | $\frac{1}{4}$ | 6·3 | D |
| 7 | 1 | $\frac{15}{64}$ | 6 | B | $\frac{9}{32}$ | 7·1 | K |
| 8 | 1·25 | $\frac{17}{64}$ | 6·7 | G | $\frac{21}{64}$ | 8·2 | P |
| 9 | 1·25 | — | 7·7 | N | $\frac{23}{64}$ | 9·2 | U |
| 10 | 1·5 | $\frac{21}{64}$ | 8·4 | Q | $\frac{11}{32}$ | 10·2 | Y |
| 11 | 1·5 | $\frac{3}{8}$ | 9·5 | V | $\frac{29}{64}$ | 11·5 | — |
| 12 | 1·75 | $\frac{13}{32}$ | 10·3 | Y | $\frac{31}{64}$ | 12·3 | — |
| 14 | 2 | $\frac{15}{32}$ | 11·9 | — | $\frac{9}{16}$ | 14·3 | — |
| 16 | 2 | $\frac{35}{64}$ | 13·8 | — | $\frac{41}{64}$ | 16·3 | — |
| 18 | 2·5 | $\frac{39}{64}$ | 15·5 | — | $\frac{23}{32}$ | 18·3 | — |
| 20 | 2·5 | $\frac{11}{16}$ | 17·5 | — | $\frac{51}{64}$ | 20·2 | — |
| 22 | 2·5 | $\frac{49}{64}$ | 19·4 | — | $\frac{7}{8}$ | 22·3 | — |
| 24 | 3 | $\frac{53}{64}$ | 21 | — | $\frac{31}{32}$ | 24·6 | — |
| 27 | 3 | $\frac{15}{16}$ | 23·8 | — | $1\frac{5}{64}$ | 27·4 | — |
| 30 | 3·5 | $1\frac{3}{64}$ | 26·5 | — | $1\frac{3}{16}$ | 30·2 | — |

Students should make special efforts to become familiar with the metric system of measurement and with the metric screw thread. They should also learn to read measuring instruments calibrated in metric units.

### The Unified thread

Before the advent of the ISO metric thread Great Britain, Canada and the United States adopted a standardized thread form known as the Unified thread (Fig. 6.8.). This has a thread angle of 60° and in the male form (bolts, set-screws, and studs) both crests and roots are rounded. In the female form (nuts and tapped holes) the roots are rounded while the crests are left flat.

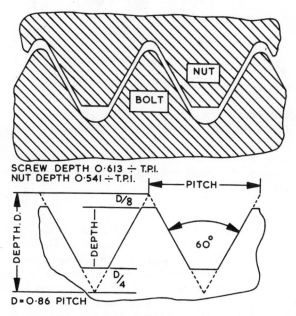

Fig. 6.8 Basic unified thread

**Tapping and clearance sizes.** For most practical purposes the Unified and the AF threads are interchangeable. The drilling sizes for the AF threads also suit those of the Unified threads.

*Identification*

While the Unified thread can be interchanged with the AF threads it most definitely *cannot be interchanged with British or metric threads*. Many threads on British vehicles are now of the Unified form and these are marked for easy identification in the following ways (Fig. 6.9):

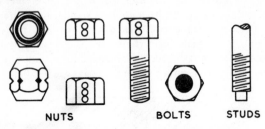

**NUTS**          **BOLTS**          **STUDS**

Fig. 6.9 Identification of unified threads

(1) Bolts and set-screws – a circular depression formed in the top of the head or connected circles stamped on one of the flat sides of the head.

(2) Studs – the end machined down to the core diameter of the thread.

(3) Nuts – connected circles in one face or a circular groove turned in the top face. Wheel nuts are marked by notches in the centres of the face corners.

**Self-tapping screws**

These screws are widely used in modern vehicles for all kinds of temporary fastening where light loads are involved. They have a large variety of head shapes and are often chromium plated. Also, they are extremely hard and cut their own threads as they are initially screwed home, the thread being tapered and rather like that of a wood screw. They are generally used to connect sheet metal sections. The table below gives the tapping drill sizes required:

| Size No. | | 2 | 4 | 6 | 8 | 10 | 12 | 14 |
|---|---|---|---|---|---|---|---|---|
| Tapping Drill | No. | 49 | 39 | 35 | 31 | 27 | 19 | 11 |
| | mm | 1·85 | 2·55 | 2·8 | 3·0 | 3·7 | 4·2 | 4·9 |

*Rough methods of finding tapping drill sizes*

These are rule-of-thumb or rough-and-ready methods of finding the very approximate drill sizes for tapping. They should not be used except in emergency and care must be taken to make a close estimate of the correct drill.

(1) Try different sizes of drill in a *new nut*. The drill which will just pass through the nut is the one to use as the tapping size drill.

(2) Hold the correct tap against the light and place different sizes of drill behind it. The drill which just covers the core diameter but leaves the threads showing clearly is the one to use.

Both of these methods, if carefully done, will give a reasonably strong thread when the hole is tapped.

## Taps and dies

*Taps*

The tap is a hardened and tempered alloy steel tool which is used to cut an internal thread form in the correct size of drilled hole. It has a perfect thread form which is grooved or fluted along its axis to produce a series of cutting edges. The shank is left at the full diameter and has a square end to allow the fitting of the tap wrench used to turn the tap in the hole.

Taps are usually made in sets of three. One is tapered for about the first eight threads and is used to start the cutting of the thread gradually. The second tap follows the taper tap and is itself tapered for the first two or three threads. Its action deepens the thread being cut and, if the hole is clear or open at its bottom end, is used to finish the thread. If the hole is 'blind' or closed at the bottom end then the third or bottoming tap is used. This has no taper or lead at all and so cuts the full depth of thread right down to the bottom of the hole. Blind holes should be drilled one or two threads deeper than the length of thread required to allow clearance.

*Precautions in use*

(1) Taps are first fully hardened and remain very hard after tempering. They are therefore very brittle and must never be treated roughly. Keep them clean and in their grooves in the boxes. Never leave them on benches and never throw other tools upon them.

(2) Check that the drilled hole is of the correct size. If it is too large the thread will be of less than the correct depth. If it is too small the tap will not be able to cut properly and will break or produce a very broken thread form.

(3) Use the taper tap first and check that it is entering at right angles to the surface as it begins to cut. Use a small fitter's square from two directions at 90° to each other.

(4) Do not turn the tap in a single continuous movement. Ease it back after each half turn to clear the threads.

(5) Use a lubricant – cutting oil or tapping grease.

(6) Never use much force on a tap. Always ease back and clean the tap and the hole. The smaller sizes of tap are particularly easy to break.

(7) Be especially careful when tapping blind holes. Keep withdrawing the tap and clearing the bottom of the hole. Be ready for the tap bottoming and do not force it.

Where thin metal is being tapped it is a useful dodge to hold a nut of the same size over the hole and feed the taper tap into the hole through the nut. This helps to keep the tap square in a difficult job.

### Dies

The die is used to cut a thread form on an external diameter. It is a hardened and tempered alloy steel tool rather like a nut, the cutting edges being formed by four or more holes. The die is held in, and rotated by a two-handled tool called stocks. Dies may be of the split circular type or the two-part or loose die type. Both types may be adjusted to cut a slightly larger or smaller diameter of thread to suit the tapped hole. As the tapped hole cannot be adjusted in diameter it is always best to cut the tapped thread first and adjust the die thread to suit it to obtain a good fit.

As far as the precautions to be taken in their use are concerned, using a die is similar to using a tap but it is much more difficult to start the die cutting square. Usually one or two of the leading die threads are tapered and the end of the bar or tube may be tapered by filing or grinding, but great care is always needed to ensure a square start with a die. If it is not started square a 'drunken' thread form will be produced, i.e. the thread helix angle will alter along the thread. Some stocks incorporate a steadying or centralizing device to help to reduce this difficulty.

*Die nuts*

These are similar in action to the die but are not split and therefore cannot be adjusted. They are usually of square or hexagon shape and can be turned by wrenches or socket spanners in positions where a die cannot be used, e.g. on manifold studs. Die nuts are used only to clean up a damaged thread and are not suitable for the initial cutting of a thread form.

## Temporary joints

When different parts or components have to be fastened together by some form of temporary joint it is most important that the joint should remain tight until it is intentionally released. Where the correct alignment of parts is essential this may be obtained by the use of spigots and mating recesses, and/or steel dowel pins, e.g. the flywheel to the crankshaft or a brake drum to its hub. Oil seals or gaskets may be incorporated into the joint. The form of the joint, and its securing devices, are determined by the shapes and materials of the parts, the loads to which they are subjected and to the frequency with which the joint is to be disturbed in service.

The most commonly used devices for holding joint parts together are nuts and bolts, nuts and studs, and set bolts or screws. Circlips or lock-rings, which exert radial forces either internally or externally, may be used as either retaining or locating devices. Whatever the devices used to hold the joint together they must include some form of locking device to prevent the slackening of the joint by vibration or temperature changes.

Locking devices basically depend upon frictional forces or mechanical interference to prevent the rotation of nuts or bolts. If a plain nut is tightened down under a very large torque loading, the frictional forces between the threads of the nut and the stud or bolt will be large enough to prevent the nut slackening. However, this locking action soon ceases as the stud or bolt stretches under the large torque loading. Also, any vibration which occurs hastens the slackening of the nut.

In the above situation a second nut could be used to lock the first nut. This idea may be used to fit or remove studs but not for normal locking as it would be too wasteful. A special type of locknut is sometimes used, however, which is made of thin steel, pressed into shape and only one thread in depth. This is called the Palnut.

The spring washer is probably the most common locking device. It is fitted between a nut and a joint face, and consists of a split ring of hardened and tempered steel which is fitted over the bolt or stud. Spring washers are of square or rectangular cross-section and the ends are given a 'set' like a saw blade. As the nut or bolt is tightened down these ends are forced to bite into the surfaces of the nut and the component. This action both increases the friction between the threads and causes a mechanical interference or opposition to the slackening of the nut – the nut cannot turn without the spring washer cutting metal from the two faces. When the components are made from soft materials a hardened steel washer must be used under the spring washer to protect them. Many different types of spring washer are in use today, varying in the number of coils and in the arrangement of their locking teeth. One very popular range includes spring discs with radially arranged off-set teeth, the teeth being internal, external, or both.

Other frictional locking devices may be incorporated into the nut. A very successful type is that in which a fibre or nylon ring is secured into the outer face of the nut. The thread of the stud or bolt has to deform the nylon as it passes through it and this results in the nylon gripping the thread and preventing the slackening of the nut. Other self-locking nuts are slotted and the slotted portions are slightly distorted. As the nut is turned on the stud or bolt the distorted portions are forced into a slightly different position and so grip the stud thread very firmly. In all these types, if the nut can be screwed along the stud or bolt by the fingers, it should be replaced by a new nut.

A much more positive method of locking a nut is by the use of a cotter pin or split pin. These pins are made in various diameters and consist of a circular head with two long legs, each being of semicircular cross-section. After the correct torque loading has been applied to the nut the correct size of cotter pin is passed through slots in the nut and a hole drilled through the bolt, stud, or shaft. The ends of the pin legs are then bent around the nut to prevent the pin working out. The pins are made from a tough steel which can resist shear forces much larger than those normally involved in the locking of the nut. Note that this method is not suitable for use with studs which are not themselves locked into their threaded holes. In some nuts used with cotter pins the top of the nut is slotted. In other types the depth of the nut is increased to provide space for the pin without reducing the depth of the thread. These are called castle or castellated nuts, as opposed to the previously mentioned slotted nuts. These types are often used for big-end and main bearing bolts.

Slotted and castellated nuts may also be used where wire replaces cotter pins. The wire may be passed through a ring of such nuts or bolts with drilled heads, or if softer it can be twisted between two bolts. In all wire locking arrangements the wire must be so arranged that one bolt cannot slacken without the wire tightening the next bolt. The union nuts of diesel engine fuel pipes may be locked in this manner, and so may the flywheel mounting bolts.

Tab washers and lock-plates are also used to give positive locking to nuts and set bolts. Tab washers are made in many different shapes, the main ones being circular with internal and external tabs. Others consist of a tab at one side which is bent upward and another which is bent downward. Lock-plates are also made in many shapes, usually of thin steel plate with hexagonal or bi-hexagonal holes which can be fitted over two or three nuts at the same time. In another form a single nut can be locked by a plate which is held at one end by a small set screw and spring washer.

The measuring work carried out on vehicle parts is usually done to find out how much the parts have worn during a period of service. This amount of wear determines both the nature and extent of the repair work needed to make the part suitable for further use. The repair work may consist of:

(a) Restoring the part to its original dimension and shape.

(b) Making the part undersize or oversize within limits specified.

(c) Replacing an excessively worn or damaged part by a new one.

Although many workshop measurements may be taken by the use of calipers and a steel rule, the accuracy of such readings is only to about half a millimetre. Parts which must fit together with fine clearances (very small gaps) between them must be measured to a much higher standard of accuracy. One of the instruments used to obtain this higher accuracy is the micrometer, the usual workshop micrometer having an accuracy of reading of at least 0·025 mm.

### THE MICROMETER

*Principle*

The micrometer consists essentially of a screw and a U-shaped frame, the screw passing through one side of the frame. In other words, the micrometer is a screw caliper. A 16 mm metric set screw may be used to illustrate the principle of operation; if the screw is turned until its end contacts the frame, a zero position is established. In this position there is no gap between the screw and the frame. At this point one flat of the hexagonal head should be marked. If the screw is now slackened back by one full turn, a gap will be produced between the frame and the end of the screw which is the same as the pitch of the thread. A 16 mm metric thread has a pitch of 2 mm so the gap will be 2 mm. If the screw is now turned through one flat on the head, the gap will be altered by $\frac{1}{6}$ of 2 mm, or $\frac{1}{3}$ mm. This is the limit of the accuracy to which this very crude

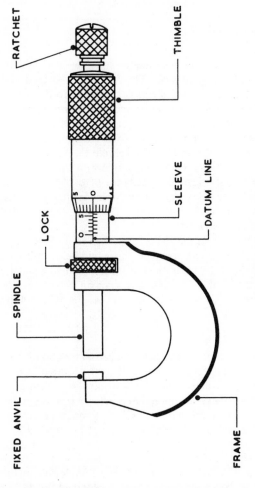

Fig. 7.1 External micrometer

instrument can measure. By selecting a screw of finer pitch and by having more divisions on the head an instrument can be made which will measure to a greater accuracy.

## The metric micrometer

### Construction

The external or caliper micrometer consists of a rigid frame of hardened and tempered steel. The frame is U-shaped and has a hardened steel disc, called the anvil, attached to the inner side of one leg of the U. A moving anvil and spindle are screwed into the opposite side of the frame so that the rotation of the spindle brings its end into contact with the fixed anvil. The spindle is rotated by a knurled, cylindrical thimble. The spindle thread has a pitch of 2 threads per millimetre. One complete turn of the spindle therefore moves the spindle through a distance of half a millimetre. The screw thread is protected by a sleeve which is attached to the frame and over which the thimble moves. The inner edge of the thimble has a wide bevelled edge.

The datum line on the sleeve is marked in millimetres and half millimetres, these being arranged above and below the line respectively. The thimble scale is marked from 0 to 50 in equal divisions. Turning the thimble through one division therefore moves the spindle through $\frac{1}{50}$ of $\frac{1}{2}$ a millimetre, or $\frac{1}{100}$ of a millimetre, or 0·01 mm.

### The ratchet

This is a small cylindrical device attached to the end of the thimble (see Fig. 7.1). The thimble should always be rotated by the ratchet which is so constructed that it will always slip when a predetermined pressure is exerted upon the spindle. In this way errors which may be caused by the different sense of touch of different individuals are avoided and the thread cannot be strained.

### Thimble lock

This is a small knurled disc set into the spindle side of the frame (see Fig. 7.1). When the correct 'feel' is obtained the disc is turned and this action clamps the spindle in the frame. By the use of this device a false reading (caused by any slight rotation of the spindle as the instrument is removed from the workpiece) is avoided. The lock should always be used, especially when passing the instrument to another person for him to check the reading.

*Reading*
The distance between the anvil and the spindle is determined by adding the sleeve reading and the thimble reading. The sleeve divisions left exposed by the thimble will be a number of millimetres and possibly a half millimetre. The thimble scale is read at the junction of the thimble-edge and the sleeve datum line and will be a number of hundredths of a millimetre.

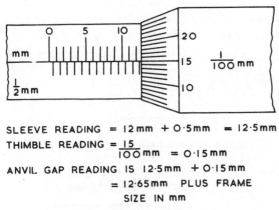

SLEEVE READING = 12 mm + 0·5 mm = 12·5 mm

THIMBLE READING = $\dfrac{15}{100}$ mm = 0·15 mm

ANVIL GAP READING IS 12·5 mm + 0·15 mm
= 12·65 mm PLUS FRAME
SIZE IN mm

Fig. 7.2 Metric micrometer

## The British micrometer

*Construction*
This is similar to the metric micrometer, the main differences being in the spindle thread and the graduations. The pitch of the spindle thread is $\frac{25}{1000}$ of an inch, i.e. there are 40 threads to the inch.

*Scale markings*
The sleeve has engraved upon it a longitudinal datum line which is divided into tenths of inches, the range of the micrometer-head normally being 1 in. These divisions are numbered from 1 to 9. Each is again divided into 4 equal parts and each part therefore represents $\frac{1}{4}$ of $\frac{1}{10}$, or, $\frac{1}{40}$, or $\frac{25}{1000}$ of an inch.

The bevelled edge of the thimble is divided into 25 equal and numbered parts, each of which represents $\frac{1}{25}$ of $\frac{1}{40}$ of an inch, or $\frac{1}{1000}$ of an inch, or 0·001 in.

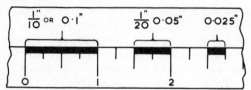

SLEEVE MARKINGS. SMALLEST DIVISION = 0·025".
THIMBLE CIRCUMFERENCE DIVIDED INTO 25
EQUAL PARTS. EACH = 0·025" ÷ 25 = 0·001"

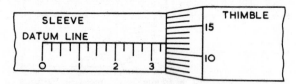

SLEEVE READING = 0·3"+0·025" = 0·325".
THIMBLE READING = 0·012".
ANVIL GAP READING IS 0·325"+0·012"
                    = 0·337" PLUS FRAME SIZE

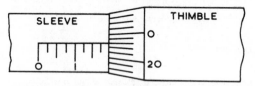

SLEEVE READING = 0·175"
THIMBLE READING = 0·023"
ANVIL GAP READING IS 0·175"+0·023"
                    = 0·198" PLUS FRAME SIZE

Fig. 7.3 Reading the micrometer

*Reading*
The gap between the anvil and the spindle-end is determined by adding together the reading taken from the sleeve and the reading

taken from the thimble. The sleeve is read to include the nearest division left exposed by the edge of the thimble; this will be the total of a number of tenths of an inch and either $\frac{25}{1000}$, $\frac{50}{1000}$ or $\frac{75}{1000}$ of an inch. The thimble scale is read at the division nearest to the sleeve datum line and will be the number of thousandths of an inch between 0 and 24.

### THE VERNIER SCALE

The term 'vernier' is commonly taken to mean the vernier caliper gauge, but it should be used to indicate a principle of subdividing small divisions of a scale. The vernier scale may be used to sub-

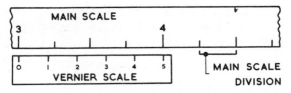

Fig. 7.4 Simple vernier

divide a main scale (as in Fig. 7.4), corresponding to the thimble of the micrometer, or it may be used to increase the accuracy of the reading of an otherwise standard instrument (as in Fig. 7.6).

*Construction*

The main features of any vernier scale are:

(1) The number of divisions on the vernier scale equals the number of parts into which the smallest division of the main scale is to be divided. For example, if the main scale division is to be divided into 5 equal parts then the vernier scale must have 5 equal divisions or parts.

(2) The total length of all the vernier scale divisions equals the length of scale taken up by this same number of main scale divisions *less one main scale division.*

In the example shown in Fig. 7.4 the difference between the length of one main scale division and one vernier division would be one fifth of a main scale division.

*Reading*

The vernier scale is read by finding a vernier marking which coincides exactly with any main scale marking. At this point the vernier marking shows the number of fifths of main scale divisions which must be added to the main scale reading. The main scale reading is read off up to the zero mark of the vernier scale, in the manner shown in Fig. 7.5.

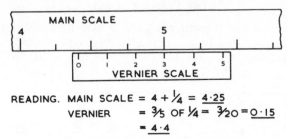

READING.  MAIN SCALE = 4 + ¼ = <u>4·25</u>
　　　　　　VERNIER　　 = ⅗ OF ¼ = ³⁄₂₀ = <u>0·15</u>
　　　　　　　　　　　　= <u>4·4</u>

Fig. 7.5 Simple vernier caliper reading

## The metric vernier micrometer

*Construction*

The metric vernier micrometer (Fig. 7.6) is a standard instrument with the addition of a vernier on the sleeve. This consists of 5 equal divisions which are parallel with the datum line and which occupy the same space as 9 thimble divisions. The difference between two thimble divisions and a vernier division therefore represents one fifth of 0·01 mm or 0·002 mm. The vernier divisions are numbered 0, 2, 4, 6, 8, 0.

*Reading*

The sleeve and thimble divisions are added to give a reading accurate to 0·01 mm. When a thimble division does not coincide exactly with the sleeve datum line, the vernier scale reading may be added to give an accuracy of 0·002 mm, the vernier scale being read at the division which coincides exactly with a thimble division.

In practice it is very difficult to read exactly to this accuracy as there are three lines which appear to coincide with the thimble division. If this accuracy is essential a strong magnifying glass should be used to help in deciding which is the coinciding division on the vernier scale.

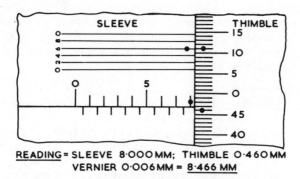

READING = SLEEVE 8·000 MM; THIMBLE 0·460 MM
VERNIER 0·006 MM = 8·466 MM

Fig. 7.6 Metric vernier micrometer

## The British vernier micrometer

*Construction*

The British vernier micrometer below is also a standard instrument with the addition of a vernier on the sleeve. This consists of 10 equal divisions which are parallel with the datum line and which occupy the same space as 9 thimble divisions. The difference between a thimble division and a vernier division therefore represents $\frac{1}{10}$ of $\frac{1}{1000}$ of an inch, or $\frac{1}{10\,000}$ in., or 0·0001 in. The vernier divisions are numbered from 1 to 9.

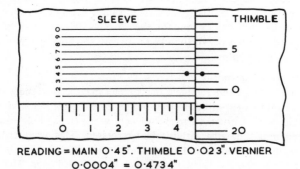

READING = MAIN 0·45". THIMBLE 0·023". VERNIER
0·0004" = 0·4734"

Fig. 7.7 British Vernier micrometer

*Reading*

The sleeve and thimble divisions are added to give a reading accurate to $\frac{1}{1000}$ of an inch. When a thimble division does not coincide exactly with the sleeve datum line, the vernier scale reading may be added to give an accuracy of $\frac{1}{10}$ of $\frac{1}{1000}$ of an inch, the vernier scale being read at the division which coincides exactly with a thimble division.

## Micrometer standards

The measuring head of the standard micrometer has a total spindle movement of only 25 mm. When dimensions in excess of 25 mm have to be measured, a range of micrometers with different frame widths is required. These usually increase in steps of 25 mm, the standard measuring head being fitted into each frame; e.g. the 25 mm micrometer will measure from 0 to 25 mm, the next size from 25 to 50 mm and so on up to about 150 mm. Special frames are available (of tubular construction) which enable measurements to be taken up to about 1 metre. The zero settings of all these instruments can only be checked by the use of standards.

The standard for the 50 mm micrometer is usually a hardened steel disc which is accurately ground to a diameter of 25 mm. When this is gripped correctly between the anvil and the spindle, the reading should be 0. Any slight adjustment which may be required should be made as described in the section dealing with micrometer adjustments.

The standards for the larger instruments consist of hardened steel rods, the ends of which are ground slightly convex. The lengths of the standards are accurate, being 50 mm for the 50 mm–75 mm instrument, 75 mm for the 75 mm–100 mm and so on. Standards must always be handled with care and held by the special grips at their centres.

## Micrometer adjustment

After considerable service a micrometer may become inaccurate as a result of wear either at the spindle thread or at the anvil and spindle faces. Thread wear is indicated when the spindle can be moved longitudinally without being rotated. This wear can be taken up or compensated by a special nut. The thimble is unscrewed to expose a circular nut which has a milled edge. This nut is fitted over a taper thread machined on the outside of the cylindrical main nut. Thus, by gently tightening the circular nut, the main nut is forced into closer contact with the spindle thread – so taking up the wear causing the slackness. After this adjustment has been made it is very important to check that the spindle can be moved freely yet has no end play.

The faces of the anvil and spindle must be flat and parallel to each other, and be at right angles to the micrometer axis. These points may be checked by cleaning the faces and bringing them together under a powerful magnifying glass. The faces can only be corrected by a specialist instrument repairer.

When the wear at the spindle thread has been corrected, and when the frame has been strained or damaged by careless handling, the accuracy of the zero setting must be checked. This should also be done when starting to use a strange instrument. The anvil and spindle faces must be cleaned and the spindle screwed down to the anvil by means of the ratchet. When the ratchet slips, the readings of both the sleeve and thimble should be zero. If this is not so the sleeve may be turned slightly on the frame (by means of a special peg spanner provided with the micrometer) until the reading is at zero. If more than a slight movement of the sleeve proves to be necessary, the probability is that the frame has been distorted and the instrument must be reconditioned or replaced.

**Special micrometers**

Sometimes dimensions must be taken in situations where a standard micrometer cannot provide an accurate reading because of the shape of its frame or anvils. Special micrometers have been designed for use in these situations and a few examples are listed below.

*The screw-thread micrometer*, Fig. 7.8

This is a caliper micrometer in which the anvil is vee-shaped and the spindle end is a rounded and tapering point. Each instrument

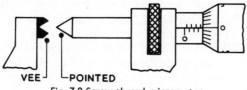

VEE  POINTED
Fig. 7.8 Screw-thread micrometer

is suitable only for a limited range of thread forms and sizes, so a number of separate instruments are needed to cover a reasonable range of threads.

*The tube micrometer*, Fig. 7.9
This is another form of caliper micrometer, in which the anvil is hemispherical while the spindle end is flat. This type is designed to measure the wall thickness of tubes and pipes.

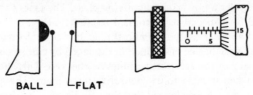

BALL　　　FLAT

Fig. 7.9 Tube type micrometer

*The sheet metal micrometer*
This has a very deep, U-shaped frame with a flat-ended anvil and spindle. It permits measurements to be taken at points well in from the rough edges of metal sheets.

*The internal micrometer*, Fig. 7.10
This is designed to measure the internal diameter of bores larger than about 40 mm. It is probably the special micrometer of most value to the motor engineer.
*Construction*. The measuring head is similar in construction to that of the caliper micrometer but it has a range of either 13 mm or 25 mm. The accuracy is either 0·01 or 0·002 mm. The ratchet is replaced by a small, spherical-ended anvil while the spindle and sleeve are combined and comparatively short. The sleeve is so constructed that different lengths of extension rod may be fitted into it to increase the range of the instrument. Each rod is marked to indicate the lengths which may be measured when it is fitted into the head. It is most important that the rods be clean and correctly fitted. Shoulders and locating marks are provided to assist in their correct assembly. A small knurled screw is used to lock the rods into the sleeve, and a handle may be screwed into the sleeve (at right angles to its axis) to enable the micrometer to be used inside a long bore.

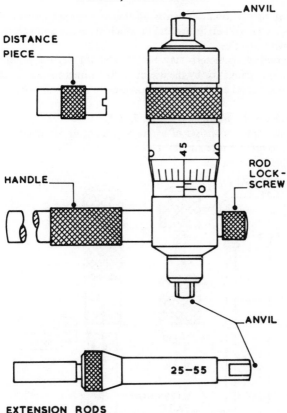

DISTANCE PIECE

ANVIL

HANDLE

ROD LOCK-SCREW

ANVIL

EXTENSION RODS

25–55

Fig. 7.10 Internal micrometer

*Scales and reading.* The scales are read in the same manner as those of the standard micrometer. It should be noted that when the internal micrometer is reading 0 the overall length is about 50 mm. Bores which have a diameter less than the length of this instrument must therefore be measured by some other instrument such as a telescopic gauge or a special dial gauge.

The internal micrometer has no ratchet and its accuracy of reading depends upon the sense or feel of the user. Great care must always be taken to avoid straining the spindle thread or bending the rods. A light rubbing touch is all that is required and obtaining this is a trial-and-error process in which accuracy and speed come only with practice.

Internal micrometers may be checked for accuracy either by setting ring gauges or by the use of a caliper micrometer which has itself been checked and found accurate.

*The micrometer depth gauge*, Fig. 7.11

This instrument consists of a micrometer-head arranged at right angles to an accurate and flat base. It is a more accurate version of a simple depth gauge.

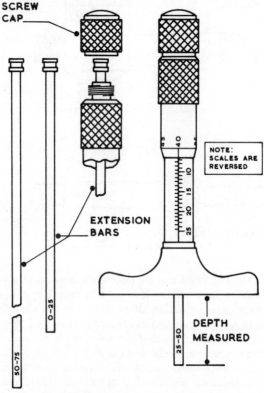

Fig. 7.11 Metric micrometer depth gauge

*The adjustable micrometer*, Fig. 7.12

This is a caliper micrometer which has a large frame into which may be fitted anvils of alternative length. In some circumstances this type may be preferable to having a number of separate instruments, but generally the size of the frame limits its use to

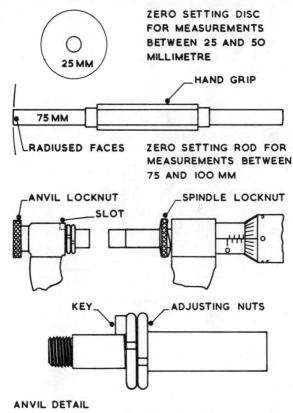

ZERO SETTING DISC
FOR MEASUREMENTS
BETWEEN 25 AND 50
MILLIMETRE

25 MM

HAND GRIP

75 MM

RADIUSED FACES

ZERO SETTING ROD FOR
MEASUREMENTS BETWEEN
75 AND 100 MM

ANVIL LOCKNUT

SLOT

SPINDLE LOCKNUT

KEY

ADJUSTING NUTS

ANVIL DETAIL

Fig. 7.12 Adjustable micrometer

work which can be measured on the bench. The anvils are inter-changeable in the frame and differ in steps of 25 mm. The same care and precautions must be taken with these anvils as with the setting rods of the internal micrometer and with the micrometer standards.

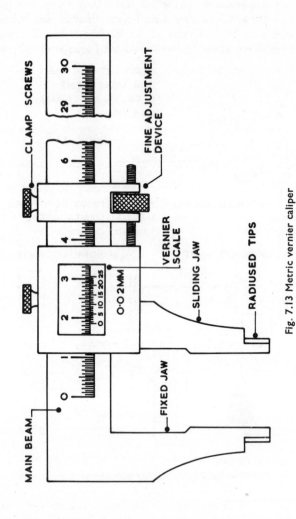

Fig. 7.13 Metric vernier caliper

## The metric vernier caliper

*Construction*

The metric vernier caliper (Fig. 7.13) consists of a main beam of rectangular section with an integral fixed jaw. The beam is marked with a scale graduated into millimetres and half millimetres. A second jaw is mounted upon the beam and can be moved along it. This sliding jaw has a clamp screw and a fine adjustment device, and its frame is marked by a vernier scale.

*Scales*, Fig. 7.14

The main scale is divided into millimetres and half millimetres; i.e. the smallest division is 0·5 mm. The length of the vernier scale is equal to 24 of these main scale divisions (12 mm) and is itself divided into 25 equal parts. A vernier division therefore represents $\frac{12}{25}$ or 0·48 mm and the difference between a main scale and a vernier division is 0·02 mm (0·5 mm less 0·48 mm).

*Use*

The component or thickness to be measured is placed between the jaws of the caliper and the sliding jaw closed up to obtain an approximately correct feel. The fine adjustment device is then clamped to the beam and the sliding jaw moved by the fine adjustment screw until the correct feel is obtained. The sliding jaw is then clamped to the beam and the caliper removed for reading.

Outside measurements may be taken by reading the length between the inner faces of the jaws. Internal measurements may be taken by reading the length between the radiused outer faces of the jaws. Some instruments have a second scale on the reverse side of the beam which enables internal measurements to be read off directly. If there is no second scale the width of the jaws must be added to the scale reading. This width may be marked upon the jaws or may be measured by means of an accurate micrometer.

*Reading*

The main scale is read off up to the zero of the vernier scale and consists of millimetres and possibly a half millimetre (see Fig. 7.14). The vernier scale is read off at the division which coincides exactly with a main scale division. This vernier scale reading is the number of 0·02 mm which must be added to the main scale reading, so *the number read off the vernier scale must be multiplied by two.*

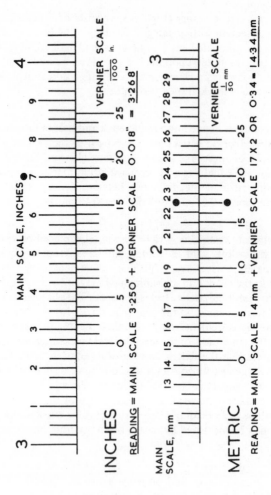

Fig. 7.14 Vernier caliper scales

*Note*. In another form of metric vernier the main scale is divided into millimetres only. The vernier scale is equal in length to 49 main scale divisions and is divided into 50 equal parts. Once again the difference between a main scale and a vernier scale division is 0·02 mm and the vernier reading must be multiplied by 2 to give the decimal fraction of millimetres which must be added to the main scale reading.

### The British vernier caliper

This is similar in construction to the vernier caliper (described previously). The beam scale is divided into inches, tenths and fortieths of an inch.

*Scales*, Fig. 7.14

The smallest division on the beam is $\frac{1}{40}$ of an inch or 0·025 in. The length of the vernier scale is equal to that of 24 of these divisions and is divided into 25 equal parts. Every fifth division is numbered. The difference between the length of a beam division and a vernier division is therefore $\frac{1}{25}$ of $\frac{1}{40}$ of an inch, or $\frac{1}{1000}$ in., or 0·001 in.

*Reading*

The dimension required is the total of the beam and vernier scale readings. The main scale is read to give the number of inches, tenths, and fortieths of inches up to the zero of the vernier scale. The vernier scale is read in thousandths of inches at the point where a vernier line and a main scale line coincide.

### Vernier adjustment

After prolonged use the vernier caliper may become inaccurate due to the wearing of the jaw faces. A slight inaccuracy may be detected by cleaning the jaws and bringing them together when the reading on both scales will not be zero. This may be corrected by releasing the vernier scale attachment screws and moving the scale on its frame until the zero marks coincide exactly. The screws are then tightened and the zero rechecked.

If more than this slight adjustment is necessary the jaws may have worn tapered, or have been strained. In this case the instrument must be replaced or reconditioned.

**The vernier depth gauge**

*Construction*

The simple gauge consists of a narrow but rigid steel rule about 150 mm long which slides in a groove machined in one side of a heavier steel body. The upper and lower faces of the body are accurately ground flat and are at 90° to the axis of the rule. The rule is secured to the body by means of an adjustable clamp screw. A vernier scale is engraved upon the body.

*Scales*

The rule is marked in millimetres. The vernier scale is 9 mm long and is divided into ten equal divisions. Each vernier division therefore represents $\frac{1}{10}$ mm or 0·1 mm.

*Reading*

The rule is read up to the vernier scale zero. The vernier is read at the division coinciding with a rule division and the two readings are added together.

**The simple protractor,** Fig. 7.15

Protractors are used to measure, compare and mark out angles.

One good form of simple protractor consists of an accurately-machined rectangular plate which is engraved with a semicircular scale. The scale is graduated from 0° to 180° in both directions.

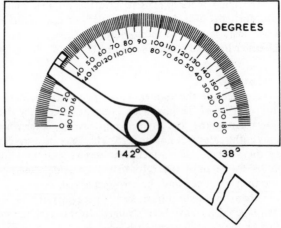

Fig. 7.15 Simple protractor

Pivoted at the centre of the scale (by means of a clamp screw) is a blade which extends back to sweep over the scale. The extension carries a fine line which lies on the axis of the blade and simplifies the setting and reading of the instrument.

With care this instrument can be used to an accuracy of 1°. If greater accuracy is needed the vernier protractor must be used.

**The vernier protractor,** Fig. 7.16

*Construction*

In engineering the accurate measurement of angles is always a difficult task and, because the instruments used must be relatively small, small errors are magnified as the distance from the point of the angle is increased. Possible errors may be reduced by the use of a vernier scale which will provide an accuracy of 5 minutes or $\frac{1}{12}$ of a degree.

READING CLOCKWISE 23° 0'

Fig. 7.16 Vernier protractor

*Scales*

Most protractors are graduated to read up to 90° on each side of a common zero. The vernier scale is also arranged in two parts about a common zero and great care must always be taken to read the vernier scale *in the same direction* as the main scale.

To reduce the difficulty of reading a large number of very small divisions, 12 vernier scale divisions are made equal in length to 23 protractor scale divisions; so one vernier division is $\frac{1}{12}$ of a degree, or 5 minutes, shorter than two protractor divisions. One vernier divisions therefore represents 5 minutes. Each side of the double vernier scale is marked from 0 to 60 in 15-minute major divisions.

## Reading

Note the number of degrees on the protractor scale up to the zero of the vernier scale. Reading *in the same direction* add to this the number of minutes on the vernier scale between the vernier zero and the vernier division which coincides exactly with a protractor division.

## Feeler gauges

### Construction

These consist of a number of hardened and tempered, polished and flexible, steel blades. Their thicknesses vary from about 0·03 mm to about 0·5 mm. A set does not include every intermediate size but the selection is so arranged that by combining different blades all the sizes normally required are available. The blades are fastened into a steel frame by a rivet or a screw and are usually about 100 mm long and 13 mm wide. Their free ends are often tapered down in width to about 6 mm. The thickness of each blade, in millimetres, is engraved upon it.

### Use

Feeler gauges are used to determine accurately the size of small gaps or clearances between parts. Feelers are essential tools in vehicle work and are used for setting valve clearances, contact-breaker points, piston-ring gaps, and for checking crankshaft end-float. Special forms of feeler gauge are used for checking the piston-to-cylinder-bore clearance in some engines. The cylindrical form feeler gauge should be used in checking and adjusting sparking-plug points.

### Precautions

(1) Keep the blades lightly oiled and free from grit, water and rust.
(2) Always use the minimum possible number of blades.
(3) Avoid the trapping and twisting of the blades.
(4) Never exceed a light but firm feel or grip on the blades.

## The combination square

The combination square (Fig. 7.17) consists of a very rigid

rule which can be fitted into any one of three different heads to provide three different instruments. The rule can be obtained with different graduations to suit the work being carried out; i.e. English or metric units, or a combination with inches and metric units.

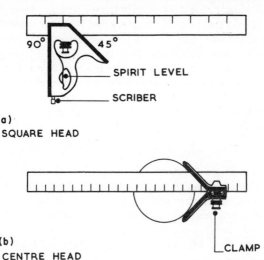

(a)
SQUARE HEAD

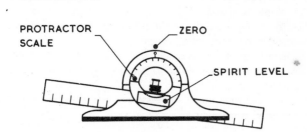

(b)
CENTRE HEAD

(c)
PROTRACTOR HEAD

Fig. 7.17 Combination set

The rule has a groove machined along its longitudinal axis which engages with a pegged and slotted clamp screw built into each head.

When the rule is attached to the square head, Fig. 7.17(a), the combination or assembly provides an instrument which can be used as a square or for marking out 45° angles. The square head is also fitted with a spirit level, and in some types also has a small scriber which is screwed into the head when not in use.

The centre head, Fig. 7.17(b), is in the form of a right-angled vee and the rule is fitted in such a manner that the angle is bisected by one edge of the rule. This forms a very useful tool for marking out the centre of round or cylindrical workpieces.

The protractor head, Fig. 7.17(c), is graduated to read from 0° to 180° in both directions and includes a spirit level. This combination is very useful both for marking out and alignment checking.

Although this instrument is a very useful piece of workshop equipment its use is not recommended for the checking of very accurate work.

### Care of measuring instruments

Measuring instruments are very carefully designed and manufactured and, given fair and proper treatment, will give good service for many years. It is false economy to buy cheap instruments which cannot possibly provide the necessary accuracy nor have a very long life. Precision instruments must be handled gently and used properly to protect both them and the work they are checking from possible inaccuracies.

The following precautions should always be taken when using measuring instruments of all types:

(1) Clean both the measuring faces of the instrument and the workpiece very carefully to remove all dirt, oil, and metal chips.

(2) Check the instrument for accuracy before using. Adjust and re-check, if necessary.

(3) Do not use on any moving surface.

(4) Do not hold the instrument in the hands for longer than is necessary. The heat of the hand is sufficient to cause an expansion which will affect the accuracy of the reading.

(5) Keep the measuring faces at right angles to the workpiece.

(6) Avoid excessive pressures on micrometer spindles – use the ratchet. Do not overstrain the fine adjustment device on the vernier caliper.

(7) Do not use measuring instruments for any purpose for which they were not designed.

(8) Do not throw precision instruments down on to the bench – keep them apart from ordinary tools and always return them to their cases when not actually in use.

(9) Keep all measuring instruments away from dirt and grease.

(10) Clean after use and give a thin film of a non-corrosive oil. Return to store in good condition or report any damage.

### LIMITS, FITS AND CLEARANCES

**Limits**

In the very early days of engineering the method used to ensure the correct fitting together of two parts was to make one part first and then machine the other to suit it. This method may be practicable where a small number of parts is involved, and where replacements are very seldom required. When large numbers of parts have to be produced, as in almost every production factory today, this method cannot be used because (a) it is too slow, (b) it is too expensive, and (c) the parts are all slightly different and cannot be interchanged without further machining or hand fitting. The modern method of cheaper, mass production is to permit small variations in machining; i.e. parts are allowed to vary from their theoretical or nominal size by a certain small and limited amount.

As an example, an engine designer may say that the crankpins of a certain crankshaft should be 50 mm in diameter. Apart from it being impossible to machine to a very exact size he knows that in practice a very high degree of accuracy will result in slow production, more scrap and higher costs. He also knows that this accuracy is not essential either to the operation or to the interchangeability of the crankshaft. The result is that he specifies a nominal diameter of 50 mm and then lays down acceptable upper and lower limits of small variations from this size; e.g. the upper limit might be 50·013 mm and the lower limit 49·987 mm, see Fig. 7.18(a). This would be written down as 50 mm plus or minus $\frac{13}{1000}$ mm, or 50 mm $\pm$ 0·013 mm.

**Tolerance**

The difference between the upper and lower limits of the permitted variation from the nominal size is called the *tolerance*, see Fig. 7.18(a). Tolerances may be allowed either on one side only of the nominal size or across the nominal size as in the example

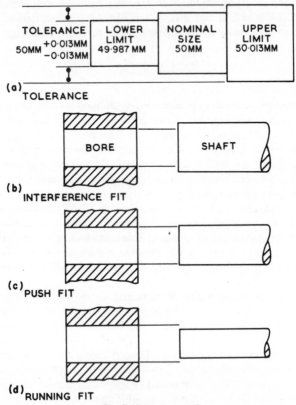

Fig. 7.18 Limits and fits

just given. All work which does not fall within the given limits must be rejected and either rectified or scrapped. Although limits are used in almost every machining and fitting operation they assume greater importance where shafts and holes, or bearings, are to be assembled.

## Classes of fits

There are a number of different classes of fit associated with shafts and bearings, and with similar parts which fit together. These are:

**(1) Interference, force, or shrink fits.** The characteristic of these fits is that the shaft is slightly larger in diameter than the hole or bearing into which it is to be fitted, see Fig. 7.18(b). Force or heat must be used to obtain the correct assembly and it is unlikely that the parts will be separated except for replacement. Examples are valve-seat inserts and flywheel ring gears. The interference is the amount by which the shaft diameter exceeds the bore diameter at normal temperature.

**(2) Driving fits.** These are a form of interference fit in which less force is required for assembly because the shaft diameter is closer to the size of the hole; i.e. there is a smaller amount of interference.

**(3) Push fits,** Fig. 7.18(c). In these the force required for assembly is very small. This fit is used for parts which are detachable; e.g. dowel pins and their mating holes, and some spigot joints.

**(4) Running fits,** Fig. 7.18(d). The characteristic of this large class of fit is that a gap or clearance exists between the two parts; i.e. the shaft diameter is less than that of the hole. The size of the clearance depends upon a number of factors such as the speed of movement between the parts, the loads imposed upon them, the nature of their materials, and the presence or absence of a lubricant. The clearance is the space between the shaft and the hole or bearing.

# Appendix

### The SI system of units

The traditional systems of measurement, which have no logical basis or relationships, are being replaced in most countries by the modern form of the metric system. This is the Système Internationale d'Unités (SI system) in which each unit can be accurately defined and is universally applicable. The multiples and sub-multiples of each unit are arranged in steps of ten, although in practice they are used in steps of one thousand, e.g. the unit of length is the metre (m), the multiple used is the kilometre (km) or 1000 m, and the sub-multiple is the millimetre (mm) or $\frac{1}{1000}$ m.

There are six basic units in the SI system – the metre (m) for length, the kilogramme (kg) for mass, the newton (N) for force, the second (s) for time, the ampere (A) for electric current, the Kelvin (K) for absolute temperature, and the candela (cd) for luminous intensity. Temperature is ordinarily measured in degrees Celsius (°C). All other SI units are derived from these six basic units, e.g. the unit of area is the square metre ($m^2$), the unit of acceleration is the metre per second per second ($m/s^2$), and the unit of pressure is the newton per square metre ($N/m^2$). The newton is defined as the force which, when applied to a body of unit mass (1 kg), gives it an acceleration of one metre per second per second (unit acceleration 1 $m/s^2$).

Under the SI system clearances and settings are specified in decimal fractions of millimetres, petrol is supplied by the litre, speedometers are calibrated in kilometres per hour, and pressures measured in kilonewtons per square metre ($kN/m^2$) or a unit derived from this multiple. The changeover to the SI system will take several years and, until all design and production is converted to SI, it will be necessary for everyone to be able to use both Imperial and SI units for some time to come.

Tables and slide rules are available for conversions from Imperial to SI but the new system will not be fully effective until everyone can think in the new units, e.g. visualise a metre and a millimetre, or any other common everyday unit. Students are therefore advised to make themselves familiar with the SI units and their relationships as soon as possible.

The most commonly used prefixes denoting multiples or sub-multiples of the basic units are the following:

| Prefix | Symbol | Unit multiplied by: | Example |
|--------|--------|---------------------|---------|
| mega | M | one million ($10^6$) | megawatt (MW) |
| kilo | k | one thousand ($10^3$) | kilometre (km) |
| hecto | h | one hundred ($10^2$) | hectogramme (hg) |
| deca | da | ten ($10^1$) | decagramme (dag) |
| | | *Unit divided by:* | |
| deci | d | ten ($10^{-1}$) | decimetre (dm) |
| centi | c | one hundred ($10^{-2}$) | centimetre (cm) |
| milli | m | one thousand ($10^{-3}$) | millimetre (mm) |
| micro | $\mu$ | one million ($10^{-6}$) | micrometre or micron ($\mu$m) |

A sub-unit of particular interest to mechanics is the cubic deci-metre ($dm^3$) for which the new system allows use of the term 'litre' for ordinary purposes such as petrol measurement, although not for precise measurements; the litre is minutely larger than the cubic decimetre ($1 \cdot 000028 \ dm^3$).

### THE METRIC SYSTEM

## Units of length

| Unit | Abbreviation | Equivalent measure |
|------|--------------|--------------------|
| Millimetre* | mm | 1/1000 metre |
| Centimetre | cm | 1/100  metre |
| Decimetre | dm | 1/10  metre |
| Metre* | m | 1 metre |
| Decametre | Dm | 10   metres |
| Hectometre | Hm | 100   metres |
| Kilometre* | km | 1000   metres |
| Myriametre | Mm | 10000 metres |

## Units of area

| Unit | Abbreviation | Equivalent measure |
|------|--------------|--------------------|
| Centare* | ca | 1    square metre ($m^2$) |
| Are | ar | 100   square metres ($m^2$) |
| Hectare | har | 10000 square metres ($m^2$) |

## Units of capacity

| Unit | Abbreviation | Equivalent measure |
|------|--------------|--------------------|
| Millilitre | ml | 1/1000 litre |
| Centilitre | cl | 1/100  litre |
| Decilitre | dl | 1/10  litre |
| Litre* | l | 1  litre |
| Decalitre | Dl | 10   litres |
| Hectolitre | Hl | 100   litres |
| Kilolitre | kl | 1000   litres |
| Hectostere | Hs | 10000 litres |

## Units of mass

| Unit | Abbreviation | Equivalent measure |
|------|--------------|--------------------|
| Milligramme | mg | 1/1000 gramme |
| Centigramme | cg | 1/100  gramme |
| Decigramme | dg | 1/10  gramme |
| Gramme | g | 1 gramme |
| Decagramme | Dg | 10   grammes |
| Hectogramme | Hg | 100   grammes |
| Kilogramme* | kg | 1000   grammes |
| Myriagramme | Mg | 10000 grammes |

* These are S I units

CONVERSION TABLES

## Units of length

*British to metric.* Based upon 1 in = 25·4 mm and approximated to two figures. 10 mm = 1 cm; 10 cm = 1 m; 1000 m = 1 km.

| Inches | Millimetres | Feet | Metres | Miles | Kilometres |
|--------|-------------|------|--------|-------|------------|
| ¼ | 6·35 | **1** | **0·305** | **1** | **1·61** |
| ½ | 12·7 | 2 | 0·61 | 2 | 3·22 |
| ¾ | 19·05 | 3 | 0·91 | 3 | 4·83 |
| **1** | **25·4** | 4 | 1·22 | 4 | 6·44 |
| 2 | 50·8 | 5 | 1·52 | 5 | 8·05 |
| 3 | 76·2 | 6 | 1·83 | 6 | 9·66 |
| 4 | 101·6 | 7 | 2·13 | 7 | 11·27 |
| 5 | 127·0 | 8 | 2·44 | 8 | 12·88 |
| 6 | 152·4 | 9 | 2·74 | 9 | 14·49 |
| 7 | 177·8 | 10 | 3·05 | 10 | 16·10 |
| 8 | 203·2 | 25 | 7·62 | 25 | 40·25 |
| 9 | 228·6 | 50 | 15·24 | 50 | 80·50 |
| 10 | 254·0 | 75 | 22·86 | 75 | 120·75 |
| 11 | 279·4 | 100 | 30·48 | 100 | 161·00 |
| 12 | 304·8 | | | | |

*Fractions of an inch to millimetres*

| Inches | | Millimetres | Inches | | Millimetres |
|--------|--|-------------|--------|--|-------------|
| 1/64 | 0·015625 | 0·3969 | 9/64 | 0·140625 | 3·5719 |
| 1/32 | 0·031250 | 0·7938 | 5/32 | 0·156250 | 3·9688 |
| 3/64 | 0·046875 | 1·1906 | 11/64 | 0·171875 | 4·3656 |
| 1/16 | 0·062500 | 1·5875 | 3/16 | 0·187500 | 4·7625 |
| 5/64 | 0·078125 | 1·9844 | 13/64 | 0·203125 | 5·1594 |
| 3/32 | 0·093750 | 2·3813 | 7/32 | 0·218750 | 5·5563 |
| 7/64 | 0·109375 | 2·7781 | 15/64 | 0·234375 | 5·9531 |
| 1/8 | 0·125000 | 3·1750 | 1/4 | 0·250000 | 6·3500 |

*Fractions of an inch to millimetres – continued*

| Inches | | Millimetres | Inches | | Millimetres |
|---|---|---|---|---|---|
| 17/64 | 0·265625 | 6·7469 | 41/64 | 0·640625 | 16·2719 |
| 9/32 | 0·281250 | 7·1438 | 21/32 | 0·656250 | 16·6688 |
| 19/64 | 0·296875 | 7·5406 | 43/64 | 0·671875 | 17·0656 |
| 5/16 | 0·312500 | 7·9375 | 11/16 | 0·687500 | 17·4625 |
| 21/64 | 0·328125 | 8·3344 | 45/64 | 0·703125 | 17·8594 |
| 11/32 | 0·343750 | 8·7313 | 23/32 | 0·718750 | 18·2563 |
| 23/64 | 0·359375 | 9·1281 | 47/64 | 0·734375 | 18·6531 |
| 3/8 | 0·375000 | 9·5250 | 3/4 | 0·750000 | 19·0500 |
| 25/64 | 0·390625 | 9·9219 | 49/64 | 0·765625 | 19·4469 |
| 13/32 | 0·406250 | 10·3188 | 25/32 | 0·781250 | 19·8438 |
| 27/64 | 0·421875 | 10·7156 | 51/64 | 0·796875 | 20·2406 |
| 7/16 | 0·437500 | 11·1125 | 13/16 | 0·812500 | 20·6375 |
| 29/64 | 0·453125 | 11·5094 | 53/64 | 0·828125 | 21·0344 |
| 15/32 | 0·468750 | 11·9063 | 27/32 | 0·843750 | 21·4313 |
| 31/64 | 0·484375 | 12·3031 | 55/64 | 0·859375 | 21·8281 |
| 1/2 | 0·500000 | 12·7000 | 7/8 | 0·875000 | 22·2250 |
| 33/64 | 0·515625 | 13·0969 | 57/64 | 0·890625 | 22·6219 |
| 17/32 | 0·531250 | 13·4938 | 29/32 | 0·906250 | 23·0188 |
| 35/64 | 0·546875 | 13·8906 | 59/64 | 0·921875 | 23·4156 |
| 9/16 | 0·562500 | 14·2875 | 15/16 | 0·937500 | 23·8125 |
| 37/64 | 0·578125 | 14·6844 | 61/64 | 0·953125 | 24·2094 |
| 19/32 | 0·593750 | 15·0813 | 31/32 | 0·968750 | 24·6063 |
| 39/64 | 0·609375 | 15·4781 | 63/64 | 0·984375 | 25·0031 |
| 5/8 | 0·625000 | 15·8750 | 1 | 1·000000 | 25·4000 |

*Thousandths of an inch to millimetres*

| in | mm | in | mm | in | mm | in | mm |
|---|---|---|---|---|---|---|---|
| 0·001 | 0·0254 | 0·026 | 0·6604 | 0·051 | 1·2954 | 0·076 | 1·9304 |
| 0·002 | 0·0508 | 0·027 | 0·6858 | 0·052 | 1·3208 | 0·077 | 1·9558 |
| 0·003 | 0·0762 | 0·028 | 0·7112 | 0·053 | 1·3462 | 0·078 | 1·9812 |
| 0·004 | 0·1016 | 0·029 | 0·7366 | 0·054 | 1·3716 | 0·079 | 2·0066 |
| 0·005 | 0·1270 | 0·030 | 0·7620 | 0·055 | 1·3970 | 0·080 | 2·0320 |
| 0·006 | 0·1524 | | | 0·056 | 1·4224 | | |
| 0·007 | 0·1778 | 0·031 | 0·7874 | 0·057 | 1·4478 | 0·081 | 2·0574 |
| 0·008 | 0·2032 | 0·032 | 0·8128 | 0·058 | 1·4732 | 0·082 | 2·0828 |
| 0·009 | 0·2286 | 0·033 | 0·8382 | 0 059 | 1 4986 | 0·083 | 2·1082 |
| 0·010 | 0·2540 | 0·034 | 0·8636 | 0·060 | 1·5240 | 0·084 | 2·1336 |
| | | 0·035 | 0·8890 | | | 0·085 | 2·1590 |
| 0·011 | 0·2794 | 0·036 | 0·9144 | 0·061 | 1·5494 | 0·086 | 2·1844 |
| 0·012 | 0·3048 | 0·037 | 0·9398 | 0·062 | 1·5748 | 0·087 | 2·2098 |
| 0·013 | 0·3302 | 0·038 | 0·9652 | 0 063 | 1 6002 | 0·088 | 2·2352 |
| 0·014 | 0·3556 | 0·039 | 0·9906 | 0·064 | 1·6256 | 0·089 | 2·2606 |
| 0·015 | 0·3810 | 0·040 | 1·0160 | 0·065 | 1·6510 | 0·090 | 2·2860 |
| 0·016 | 0·4064 | | | 0·066 | 1·6764 | | |
| 0·017 | 0·4318 | 0·041 | 1·0414 | 0·067 | 1·7018 | 0·091 | 2·3114 |
| 0·018 | 0·4572 | 0·042 | 1·0668 | 0·068 | 1·7272 | 0·092 | 2·3368 |
| 0·019 | 0·4826 | 0·043 | 1·0922 | 0·069 | 1·7526 | 0·093 | 2·3622 |
| 0·020 | 0·5080 | 0·044 | 1·1176 | 0·070 | 1·7780 | 0·094 | 2·3876 |
| | | 0·045 | 1·1430 | | | 0·095 | 2·4130 |
| 0·021 | 0·5334 | 0·046 | 1·1684 | 0·071 | 1·8034 | 0·096 | 2·4384 |
| 0·022 | 0·5588 | 0·047 | 1·1938 | 0·072 | 1·8288 | 0·097 | 2·4638 |
| 0·023 | 0·5842 | 0·048 | 1·2192 | 0·073 | 1·8542 | 0·098 | 2·4892 |
| 0·024 | 0·6096 | 0·049 | 1·2446 | 0·074 | 1·8796 | 0·099 | 2·5146 |
| 0·025 | 0·6350 | 0·050 | 1·2700 | 0·075 | 1·9050 | 0·100 | 2·5400 |

## Units of area

*Square inches to square centimetres (multiply by 100 for square millimetres)*

| $in^2$ | 0 | 1 | 2 | 3 | 4 |
|---|---|---|---|---|---|
| — | | 6·452 | 12·903 | 19·355 | 25·807 |
| 10 | 64·516 | 70·968 | 77·420 | 83·871 | 90·323 |
| 20 | 129·033 | 135·484 | 141·936 | 148·387 | 154·839 |
| 30 | 193·549 | 200·000 | 206·452 | 212·904 | 219·355 |
| 40 | 258·065 | 264·517 | 270·968 | 277·420 | 283·871 |
| 50 | 322·581 | 329·033 | 335·485 | 341·936 | 348·388 |
| 60 | 387·098 | 393·549 | 400·001 | 406·452 | 412·904 |
| 70 | 451·614 | 458·065 | 464·517 | 470·969 | 477·420 |
| 80 | 516·130 | 522·582 | 529·033 | 535·485 | 541·937 |
| 90 | 580·646 | 587·098 | 593·550 | 600·001 | 606·453 |

*Square inches to square centimetres – continued* (*multiply by 100 for square millimetres*)

| $in^2$ | 5 | 6 | 7 | 8 | 9 |
|---|---|---|---|---|---|
| — | 32·258 | 38·710 | 45·161 | 51·613 | 58·065 |
| 10 | 96·774 | 103·226 | 109·678 | 116·129 | 122·581 |
| 20 | 161·291 | 167·742 | 174·194 | 180·646 | 187·097 |
| 30 | 225·807 | 232·259 | 238·710 | 245·162 | 251·613 |
| 40 | 290·323 | 296·775 | 303·226 | 309·678 | 316·130 |
| 50 | 354·839 | 361·291 | 367·743 | 374·194 | 380·646 |
| 60 | 419·356 | 425·807 | 432·259 | 438·711 | 445·162 |
| 70 | 483·872 | 490·324 | 496·775 | 503·227 | 509·678 |
| 80 | 548·388 | 554·840 | 561·291 | 567·743 | 574·195 |
| 90 | 612·904 | 619·356 | 625·808 | 632·259 | 638·711 |

| British | Metric equivalent |
|---|---|
| **One square inch** | **6·45**    square centimetres |
| One square foot | 929·0  square centimetres |
| One square yard | 0·836  square metres |
| One acre | 4047    square metres |
| One square mile | 259      hectares = 2·59 square kilometres |

## Units of volume and capacity

| British | Metric equivalent |
|---|---|
| **One cubic inch** | **16·39 cubic centimetres** |
| One cubic foot | 0·03    cubic metres = $6\frac{1}{4}$ gallons |
| One cubic yard | 0·77    cubic metres |
| **One pint** | **0·56 litres** |
| One quart | 1·135 litres |
| One gallon | 4·54    litres |

*Cubic inches to cubic centimetres* (*multiply by 1000 for cubic millimetres*)

| $in^3$ | 0 | 1 | 2 | 3 | 4 |
|---|---|---|---|---|---|
| — | | **16·387** | 32·774 | 49·162 | 65·549 |
| 10 | 163·872 | 180·259 | 196·646 | 213·033 | 229·420 |
| 20 | 327·743 | 344·130 | 360·518 | 376·905 | 393·292 |
| 30• | 491·615 | 508·002 | 524·389 | 540·776 | 557·164 |
| 40 | 655·486 | 671·874 | 688·261 | 704·648 | 721·035 |
| 50 | 819·358 | 835·745 | 852·132 | 868·520 | 884·907 |
| 60 | 983·230 | 999·617 | 1016·004 | 1032·391 | 1048·778 |
| 70 | 1147·101 | 1163·489 | 1179·876 | 1196·263 | 1212·650 |
| 80 | 1310·973 | 1327·360 | 1343·747 | 1360·134 | 1376·522 |
| 90 | 1474·845 | 1491·232 | 1507·619 | 1524·006 | 1540·393 |

*Cubic inches to cubic centimetres – continued (multiply by 1000 for cubic millimetres)*

| in³ | 5 | 6 | 7 | 8 | 9 |
|---|---|---|---|---|---|
| — | 81·936 | 98·323 | 114·710 | 131·097 | 147·484 |
| 10 | 245·808 | 262·195 | 278·582 | 294·969 | 311·356 |
| 20 | 409·679 | 426·066 | 442·453 | 458·841 | 474·228 |
| 30 | 573·551 | 589·938 | 606·325 | 622·712 | 639·099 |
| 40 | 737·422 | 753·809 | 770·197 | 786·584 | 802·971 |
| 50 | 901·294 | 917·681 | 934·068 | 950·455 | 966·843 |
| 60 | 1065·166 | 1081·553 | 1097·940 | 1114·327 | 1130·714 |
| 70 | 1229·037 | 1245·424 | 1261·811 | 1278·199 | 1294·586 |
| 80 | 1392·909 | 1409·296 | 1425·683 | 1442·070 | 1458·457 |
| 90 | 1556·780 | 1573·168 | 1589·555 | 1605·942 | 1622·329 |

## Liquid measures
*Pints to litres*

| Pints | 0 | 1 | 2 | 3 | |
|---|---|---|---|---|---|
| — | — | **·568** | 1·136 | 1·705 | |
| $\frac{1}{4}$ | ·142 | ·710 | 1·279 | 1·846 | |
| $\frac{1}{2}$ | ·284 | ·852 | 1·420 | 1·989 | |
| $\frac{3}{4}$ | ·426 | ·994 | 1·563 | 2·131 | |
| Pints | 4 | 5 | 6 | 7 | 8 |
| — | 2·273 | 2·841 | 3·410 | 3·978 | 4·546 |
| $\frac{1}{4}$ | 2·415 | 2·983 | 3·552 | 4·120 | 4·688 |
| $\frac{1}{2}$ | 2·557 | 3·125 | 3·694 | 4·262 | 4·830 |
| $\frac{3}{4}$ | 2·699 | 3·267 | 3·836 | 4·404 | 4·972 |

One imperial gallon = 4·546 litres = 277 in³ = 1·2 U.S.A. or standard gallons.

One U.S.A. or standard gallon = 3·785 litres = 231 in³ = 0·833 Imperial gallons.

*Imperial gallons to litres*

| Gal | 0 | 1 | 2 | 3 | 4 |
|-----|-----|-----|-----|-----|-----|
| — | | **4·546** | 9·092 | 13·638 | 18·184 |
| 10 | 45·460 | 50·005 | 54·551 | 59·097 | 63·643 |
| 20 | 90·919 | 95·465 | 100·011 | 104·557 | 109·103 |
| 30 | 136·379 | 140·924 | 145·470 | 150·016 | 154·562 |
| 40 | 181·838 | 186·384 | 190·930 | 195·476 | 200·022 |
| 50 | 227·298 | 231·843 | 236·389 | 240·935 | 245·481 |
| 60 | 272·757 | 277·303 | 281·849 | 286·395 | 290·941 |
| 70 | 318·217 | 322·762 | 327·308 | 331·854 | 336·400 |
| 80 | 363·676 | 368·222 | 372·768 | 377·314 | 381·860 |
| 90 | 409·136 | 413·681 | 418·227 | 422·773 | 427·319 |

| Gal | 5 | 6 | 7 | 8 | 9 |
|-----|-----|-----|-----|-----|-----|
| — | 22·730 | 27·276 | 31·822 | 36·368 | 40·914 |
| 10 | 68·189 | 72·735 | 77·281 | 81·827 | 86·373 |
| 20 | 113·649 | 118·195 | 122·741 | 127·287 | 131·833 |
| 30 | 159·108 | 163·654 | 168·200 | 172·746 | 177·292 |
| 40 | 204·568 | 209·114 | 213·660 | 218·206 | 222·752 |
| 50 | 250·027 | 254·573 | 259·119 | 263·665 | 268·211 |
| 60 | 295·487 | 300·033 | 304·579 | 309·125 | 313·671 |
| 70 | 340·946 | 345·492 | 350·038 | 354·584 | 359·130 |
| 80 | 386·406 | 390·952 | 395·498 | 400·044 | 404·590 |
| 90 | 431·865 | 436·411 | 440·057 | 445·503 | 450·049 |

## Units of mass

| *British* | *Metric equivalent* | |
|-----------|------|-------------|
| One dram | 1·77 | grammes |
| One ounce | 28·35 | grammes |
| **One pound** | **453·6** | **grammes** |
| One stone | 6·35 | kilogrammes |
| One quarter | 12·7 | kilogrammes |
| One hundredweight | 50·8 | kilogrammes |
| **One ton** | **1016** | **kilogrammes** |

The British ton   = 2240 pounds   = 1016 kg = 1·016 tonnes
The metric tonne = 2204·6 pounds = 1000 kg
The short ton    = 2000 pounds   = 907·18 kg

*Pounds to kilogrammes*

| lb | 0 | 1 | 2 | 3 | 4 |
|----|------|------|------|------|------|
| — | | **0·454** | 0·907 | 1·361 | 1·814 |
| 10 | 4·536 | 4·990 | 5·443 | 5·897 | 6·350 |
| 20 | 9·072 | 9·525 | 9·979 | 10·433 | 10·886 |
| 30 | 13·608 | 14·061 | 14·515 | 14·968 | 15·422 |
| 40 | 18·144 | 18·597 | 19·051 | 19·504 | 19·958 |
| 50 | 22·680 | 23·133 | 23·587 | 24·040 | 24·494 |
| 60 | 27·216 | 27·669 | 28·123 | 28·576 | 29·030 |
| 70 | 31·751 | 32·205 | 32·659 | 33·112 | 33·566 |
| 80 | 36·287 | 36·741 | 37·195 | 37·648 | 38·102 |
| 90 | 40·823 | 41·277 | 41·731 | 42·184 | 42·638 |

| lb | 5 | 6 | 7 | 8 | 9 |
|----|------|------|------|------|------|
| — | 2·268 | 2·722 | 3·175 | 3·629 | 4·082 |
| 10 | 6·804 | 7·257 | 7·711 | 8·165 | 8·618 |
| 20 | 11·340 | 11·793 | 12·247 | 12·701 | 13·145 |
| 30 | 15·876 | 16·329 | 16·783 | 17·237 | 17·690 |
| 40 | 20·412 | 20·865 | 21·319 | 21·772 | 22·226 |
| 50 | 24·948 | 25·401 | 25·855 | 26·308 | 26·762 |
| 60 | 29·484 | 29·937 | 30·391 | 30·844 | 31·298 |
| 70 | 34·019 | 34·473 | 34·927 | 35·380 | 35·834 |
| 80 | 38·855 | 39·009 | 39·463 | 39·916 | 40·370 |
| 90 | 43·091 | 43·545 | 43·998 | 44·452 | 44·906 |

**Units of force**

1 pound force (lbf) = 4·4482 newton (N)
1 ton force (tonf) = 9964·02 newton (N)

**Units of pressure and stress**

Pressure is force per unit of cross-sectional area; the British unit is the pound per square inch (lbf/in$^2$). The metric unit is the kilo-newton per square metre (kN/m$^2$).

1 pound per square inch = 6·8948 kN/m$^2$
1 ton per square inch = 15·4443 × 10$^6$kN/m$^2$

*Pounds/square inch (lbf/in²) to kilonewton/square metre (kN/m²)*

| lbf/in² | 0 | 1 | 2 | 3 | 4 |
|---|---|---|---|---|---|
| | — | 6·8948 | 13·7895 | 20·684 | 27·579 |
| 10 | 68·948 | 75·842 | 82·737 | 89·632 | 96·527 |
| 20 | 137·895 | 144·790 | 151·685 | 158·579 | 165·474 |
| 30 | 206·84 | 213·74 | 220·63 | 227·53 | 234·42 |
| 40 | 275·79 | 282·69 | 289·58 | 296·47 | 303·37 |
| 50 | 344·74 | 351·63 | 358·53 | 365·42 | 372·32 |
| 60 | 413·69 | 420·58 | 427·47 | 434·37 | 441·26 |
| 70 | 482·63 | 489·53 | 496·42 | 503·32 | 510·21 |
| 80 | 551·58 | 558·48 | 565·37 | 572·26 | 579·16 |
| 90 | 620·53 | 627·42 | 634·32 | 641·21 | 648·11 |
| **lb/in²** | **5** | **6** | **7** | **8** | **9** |
| | 34·474 | 41·369 | 48·263 | 55·158 | 62·053 |
| 10 | 103·421 | 110·316 | 117·211 | 124·106 | 131·000 |
| 20 | 172·369 | 179·264 | 186·158 | 193·053 | 199·948 |
| 30 | 241·32 | 248·21 | 255·11 | 262·00 | 268·9 |
| 40 | 310·26 | 317·16 | 324·05 | 330·95 | 337·84 |
| 50 | 379·21 | 386·11 | 393·00 | 399·90 | 406·79 |
| 60 | 448·16 | 455·05 | 461·95 | 468·84 | 475·74 |
| 70 | 517·11 | 524·00 | 530·90 | 537·79 | 544·69 |
| 80 | 586·05 | 592·95 | 599·84 | 606·74 | 613·63 |
| 90 | 655·00 | 661·90 | 668·79 | 675·69 | 682·58 |

## Units of moments (torque)

The moment of a force is its turning effect and is calculated by multiplying the force (N) by its perpendicular distance from the point of the turn. The British unit is the pound foot and the metric unit is the newton metre.

1 pound foot $= 1·356$ newton metre (N m)

1 pound inch $= 0·1130$ newton metre

*Pound feet (lb ft) to newton metre (N m)*

| lb ft | 0 | 1 | 2 | 3 | 4 |
|---|---|---|---|---|---|
| — | — | 1·356 | 2·712 | 4·068 | 5·424 |
| 10 | 13·56 | 14·916 | 16·272 | 17·628 | 18·984 |
| 20 | 27·12 | 28·476 | 29·832 | 31·188 | 32·544 |
| 30 | 40·68 | 42·036 | 43·392 | 44·748 | 46·104 |
| 40 | 54·24 | 55·596 | 56·952 | 58·308 | 59·664 |
| 50 | 67·80 | 69·156 | 70·512 | 71·868 | 73·224 |
| 60 | 81·36 | 82·716 | 84·072 | 85·428 | 86·784 |
| 70 | 94·92 | 96·276 | 97·632 | 98·988 | 100·344 |
| 80 | 108·48 | 109·836 | 111·192 | 112·548 | 113·874 |
| 90 | 122·04 | 123·396 | 124·752 | 126·108 | 127·464 |

| lb ft | 5 | 6 | 7 | 8 | 9 |
|---|---|---|---|---|---|
| — | 6·780 | 8·136 | 9·492 | 10·848 | 12·204 |
| 10 | 20·340 | 21·696 | 23·052 | 24·408 | 25·764 |
| 20 | 33·900 | 35·256 | 36·612 | 37·968 | 39·324 |
| 30 | 47·460 | 48·816 | 50·172 | 51·528 | 52·884 |
| 40 | 61·02 | 62·376 | 63·732 | 65·088 | 66·444 |
| 50 | 74·58 | 75·936 | 77·292 | 68·648 | 80·004 |
| 60 | 88·140 | 89·496 | 90·852 | 92·208 | 93·564 |
| 70 | 101·700 | 103·056 | 104·112 | 105·768 | 107·124 |
| 80 | 115·26 | 116·616 | 117·972 | 119·328 | 120·684 |
| 90 | 128·784 | 130·176 | 131·532 | 132·888 | 134·244 |

**Velocity**

1 foot per second = 0·3048 metre per second (m/s)

1 mile per hour = 1·6093 kilometre per hour (km/h)

| mph | km/h | mph | km/h |
|-----|------|-----|------|
| 1 | 1·6093 | 25 | 40·23 |
| 2 | 3·2186 | 30 | 48·28 |
| 3 | 4·8279 | 35 | 56·3255 |
| 4 | 6·4372 | 40 | 64·3720 |
| 5 | 8·0465 | 45 | 72·4185 |
| 6 | 9·6558 | 50 | 80·465 |
| 7 | 11·2651 | 55 | 88·5115 |
| 8 | 12·8744 | 60 | 96·558 |
| 9 | 14·4837 | 65 | 104·6045x |
| 10 | 16·0930 | 70 | 112·651 |

**Acceleration**

1 foot per second per second (ft/s$^2$) = 0·3048
metre per second per second (m/s$^2$)

**Work, power, and energy**

*Work*

The joule (J) is the work done when the point of application of a
force of one newton is displaced through a distance of one metre
in the direction of the force (i.e. J = 1 N m); the watt (W) is the
unit of power equivalent to one joule per second (W = J/s).

*Energy*

1 ft lbf = 1·8556 J (joule)

1 hp h = 2·6845 MJ

1 Btu = 1·055 kJ

1 therm = 105·506 MJ

1 kW h = 3·6 MJ

1 calorie = 4·1868 J

*Power*

1 ft lbf/s = 1·3558 W (watt)

1 hp = 745·7 W

1 metric hp = 735·5 W

## CONVERSION OF TEMPERATURE SCALE

*Fahrenheit to Celsius*

To convert Fahrenheit to Celsius subtract 32 and then multiply by $\frac{5}{9}$.

| °F | °C | °F | °C | °F | °C |
|----|----|----|----|----|----|
| −15 | −26·1 | 80 | 26·7 | 195 | 90·6 |
| −10 | −23·3 | 85 | 29·4 | 200 | 93·3 |
| −5 | −20·6 | 90 | 32·2 | 205 | 96·1 |
| 0 | −17·8 | 95 | 35 | 210 | 98·9 |
| 1 | −17·2 | 100 | 37·8 | **212** | **100** |
| 2 | −16·7 | 105 | 40·6 | 215 | 101·7 |
| 3 | −16·1 | 110 | 43·3 | 220 | 104·4 |
| 4 | −15·6 | 115 | 46·1 | 225 | 107·2 |
| 5 | −15 | 120 | 48·9 | 230 | 110 |
| 10 | −12·2 | 125 | 51·7 | 235 | 112·8 |
| 15 | −9·4 | 130 | 54·4 | 240 | 115·6 |
| 20 | −6·7 | 135 | 57·2 | 245 | 118·3 |
| 25 | −3·9 | 140 | 60 | 250 | 121·1 |
| 30 | −1·1 | 145 | 62·8 | 255 | 123·9 |
| 35 | 1·7 | 150 | 65·6 | 260 | 126·6 |
| 40 | 4·4 | 155 | 68·3 | 265 | 129·4 |
| 45 | 7·2 | 160 | 71·1 | | |
| 50 | 10 | 165 | 73·9 | | |
| 55 | 12·8 | 170 | 76·7 | | |
| 60 | 15·6 | 175 | 79·4 | | |
| 65 | 18·3 | 180 | 82·2 | | |
| 70 | 21·1 | 185 | 85 | | |
| 75 | 23·9 | 190 | 87·8 | | |

### MELTING POINTS AND COEFFICIENTS OF LINEAR EXPANSION

The melting point of a substance is the temperature at which it begins to melt or fuse, changing from a solid to a liquid state.

| Material | Chemical symbol | Melting point °C | Linear expansion per degree Celsius |
|---|---|---|---|
| Aluminium | Al | 660 | 0·00002303 |
| Antimony | Sb | 630 | 0·0000114 |
| Cadmium | Cd | 320 | 0·000298 |
| Carbon | C | 3500 | 0·000008 |
| Chromium | Cr | 1616 | 0·0000082 |
| Cobalt | Co | 1480 | 0·0000123 |
| Copper | Cu | 1083 | 0·0000166 |
| Indium | In | 154 | 0·000033 |
| Cast iron | Fe | 1200 | 0·0000117 |
| Lead | Pb | 327 | 0·0000291 |
| Magnesium | Mg | 651 | 0·0000256 |
| Manganese | Mn | 1260 | 0·000023 |
| Mercury | Hg | −39 | 0·000182 |
| Molybdenum | Mo | 2621 | 0·000004 |
| Nickel | Ni | 1452 | 0·0000128 |
| Phosphorus | P | 44 | 0·000125 |
| Platinum | Pt | 1775 | 0·0000089 |
| Silicon | Si | 1420 | 0·0000028 |
| Silver | Ag | 961 | 0·0000189 |
| Sulphur | S | 113 | 0·000064 |
| Tin | Sn | 232 | 0·000020 |
| Vanadium | V | 1710 | 0·000004 |
| Zinc | Zn | 420 | 0·000033 |

There are three coefficients of expansion: linear, superficial, and cubic, i.e. of length, area, and volume. The linear coefficients are the ones usually quoted, the others being twice and three times their values respectively.

The linear coefficient of expansion is the expansion of length (increase in length) of one unit of length of the material for one degree increase in temperature. Coefficients are quoted as based upon Celsius temperature scales.

*Example.* The coefficient of linear expansion of cast iron is 0·0000117 per degree Celsius. This means that one metre of cast iron expands 0·0000117 metre when its temperature is increased by one degree Celsius.

# Index